ENERGY

CONVERSION

SHELDON S. L. CHANG

Professor of Electrical Engineering
New York University

PRENTICE-HALL, INC., ENGLEWOOD CLIFFS, N. J./1963

Library of Congress Catalog Card Number 63-10539

Printed in the United States of America

27720–C

TO MY FATHER

who believes in the goodness and future of man

PREFACE

This book on non-electromechanical energy conversion is offered as a text for an undergraduate senior course, not particularly in the belief that the conversion devices described herein will soon replace conventional generators or any substantial number of them, but rather for two other reasons:

(1) To gain a liberal technical education, students should be exposed to as many different aspects of basic knowledge as possible. At present, in the usual undergraduate electrical engineering curriculum, about half the courses (i.e., 60 to 70 credits) are devoted to electrical engineering subjects. Overwhelming emphasis is on the information-handling aspect: circuits, signal amplification, communication systems, etc. It seems only fitting to devote a course carrying at least three credits to the energy-conversion aspects of the same kinds of devices:

CORRESPONDENCE TABLE

Signal or Information-handling Devices	Corresponding Energy-conversion Devices
Semiconductor devices	Thermoelectricity
Vacuum and gaseous tubes	Thermionic converters
Gaseous tubes	MHD engines
Photoelectricity and photo cells	Photovoltaic effect and solar cells

(2) From a practical point of view, an area of technology needs and attracts engineers when it is in the developmental stage. One can be fairly certain that a substantial number of today's graduates will encounter one or another of these devices in the course of their professional careers, and some will engage in the development of these devices as their major work.

Having given the reasons for proposing a course in this general area, some remarks are in order on the selection and arrangement of material. As non-electromechanical energy conversion is a rapidly developing area, this book presents only a basic core of knowledge which is likely to be useful over the years. At first thought, one might surmise that energy conversion is a very diversified area. If so, it is so only in details, because there is a unifying principle for all types of conversion devices: the first and second laws of thermodynamics. This book emphasizes this unifying aspect.

The secondary scientific facts are indeed multitudinous. At first, the writer had intended to treat these in one or two preliminary chapters, but this plan was abandoned after trial and further careful consideration. First, such a treatment can never match a course in modern physics. Second, as the pertinent scientific facts are rather scattered and specialized, their successive presentation without due motivation appears somewhat incoherent and odd.

In lieu of the abandoned plan, this text reviews the basic ideas and concepts which are the milestones of the development of quantum mechanics and the theory of conduction (especially of semiconductors) in the present century. Since many of the pertinent facts are outgrowths of this major development, they become understandable and consistent when viewed against the theoretical background. Figuratively speaking, rather than making a survey of all the leaves on the tree of knowledge, we study the root, the trunk, and the pertinent branches. The leaves are treated in the later chapters only when they are needed for developing particular ways of energy conversion.

The plan of presenting the pertinent scientific facts as needed rather parallels the way a good research engineer works. He can never have sufficient details of sufficiently diversified knowledge committed to memory, but he must have the depth and breadth of basic scientific knowledge which enable him to look up and understand whatever he needs whenever he needs it. In working through this book, the student will have a foretaste of coming attractions if his chosen career is research or development engineering.

Finally, it is the writer's pleasure to acknowledge with thanks and appreciation the constructive suggestions and encouragement from Professors J. R. Ragazzini, J. H. Mulligan, Jr., R. Wolfson and K. Morgan of New York University, Professor J. G. Truxal of the Polytechnic Institute of Brooklyn, and Dean William L. Everitt of the University of Illinois. Special thanks are due to Miss Catherine De Fabbia, Mrs. Onna Shaw, Mrs. Rose De Luca, Mrs. Eleanor Gilmore, Mrs. Marie Trotta, and Mrs. Mary Rooney for typing the manuscript. Last but not least, the writer wishes to acknowledge his gratitude to his wife for her help and support in the writing of this book.

SHELDON S. L. CHANG

CONTENTS

ENERGY

CONVERSION

CHAPTER ONE

A SURVEY OF THE ENERGY CONVERSION PROBLEM

To gain a perspective on the energy-conversion problem, various sources of energy and their natures are discussed. Among these, the two practically unlimited sources are nuclear fusion and solar energy. Utilizing these sources, presently available methods of energy conversion already hold promise of a nearly unlimited supply of electric power at low cost.

1-1. THE PROBLEM OF POWER GENERATION

Electric power generation is perhaps one of the fields of study neglected by college students as well as their professors. For years, it has been regarded as a field without opportunity. If, however, we bring together the facts known today, it appears that in the next few decades power generation will be one of the most challenging and fertile fields of activity for future Edisons and Steinmetzes.

(1) At the present projected rate of power consumption, natural fuel deposits will be exhausted in the near future. To illustrate this point, we quote the following passages from J. A. Hutcheson's paper, "Engineering for the Future":*

Our scientists and engineers are seeking new ways to obtain electric power from a variety of prime sources of energy. But most of it today comes from the burning

---

* J. A. Hutcheson, "Engineering for the Future", *Journal of Engineering Education*, Vol. **50**, No. 8, April 1960, pp. 602–607.

of fuels deposited in the earth countless millions of years ago. In fact, at the present time, essentially all our energy, for whatever purpose we use it, comes from fossil fuels, including coal, gas and petroleum. Together these sources account for 96% of our energy supply. Almost all the remaining 4% comes from water power.

It is pertinent to look at the world resources of fossil fuels. We find that estimates of these reserves vary widely, so to make use of them, I have chosen to take both the most optimistic and the most pessimistic estimates. Thus, if we translate all fossil fuels into the equivalent number of tons of coal, the most optimistic estimate of the world's resources places them at 8,000 billion metric tons; the most pessimistic estimate is ten times smaller. At the present world rate of consumption of energy, the time for exhaustion of the world's reserves is 4,000 years optimistically, or 400 years pessimistically.

It must be emphasized that these estimates are based on the consumption of energy by the peoples of the world at current rates. These figures allow nothing for increase in world population or for a rising standard of living throughout the world. Today's world population is over 2.6 billion. By 1980, United Nations estimates place it at 3.6 billion. Suppose a world population of even 3 billion wanted to achieve a standard of living comparable to that which you and I enjoy today. In such case, the optimistic estimate of our fuel reserves drops from 4,000 to 230 years, and the pessimistic estimate drops from 400 to 23 years.

One cannot predict what factors will affect this situation. But it simply is being realistic to recognize that the trend is such that by the end of this century the problem of a supply of energy to maintain our standard of living may well be acute. Whatever the answer may be—fusion, or sources of power yet to be discovered— certainly man's voracious, frequently wasteful appetite for energy must be of increasing concern to the engineer of tomorrow.

(2) In conjunction with the space science program, other basic methods of generating electricity have been investigated and successfully implemented on space vehicles. These methods could become more feasible than the present steam turbines and generators when nuclear fission and fusion become prime sources of power. Current research in alloy and semiconductor materials also tends to improve the relative feasibility of the newer methods.

(3) As electricity is the one and only form of energy "that is easy to make, easy to transport, easy to use, and easy to control,"* it will continue to be the terminal form of energy for transmission and distribution.

In other words, it is more than likely that we shall see a revolutionary change in the basic industry of power generation in our time because of a shortage of traditional fuel. This pressing need for new ways of generating energy has stimulated present scientific thought. Because the source of fusion energy is practically inexhaustible, the same opportunity for stimu-

---

* J. A. Hutcheson, "Engineering for the Future", *Journal of Engineering Education*, Vol. 50, No. 8, April 1960, pp. 602–607.

lating scientific investigation will probably not arise again in the entire epoch of human tenancy on this planet.

1-2. SOURCES OF ENERGY

The primary sources of energy can be classified into the following categories:

1. Solar
2. Hydraulic
3. Chemical
4. Nuclear

Here *solar energy* is used in its restricted sense of direct radiation. In a broader sense, hydraulic energy can be considered as solar energy stored within the past few weeks, whereas fossil fuel or chemical energy can be considered as solar energy stored in the past millions or billions of years.

The immense magnitude of direct solar energy can be illustrated by the following estimate: Measurements show that the intensity of solar radiation at sea level on North American continent in the summer is approximately 1 kw/m². As the normal surface of the earth presented to the sun is πR^2, where R is the radius of the earth, the total solar energy at sea level is approximately

$$1 \text{ kw}/m^2 \times \pi \times (3960 \text{ miles})^2 \times (1610 \text{ m/mile})^2 = 1.28 \times 10^{14} \text{ kw}$$

If 0.1% of the earth's surface is used for converting solar energy to electrical energy at an efficiency of 5% (a figure well below that of some available solar cells), the electrical energy generated yearly is

$$1.28 \times 10^{14} \text{ kw} \times 0.001 \times 0.05 \times 24 \times 365 = 5.6 \times 10^{13} \text{ kwh}$$

which is still about forty times the present annual rate of consumption of the whole world.

Another interesting comparison is that the total fossil energy on earth is less than the solar energy incident upon earth in one year.

As the first three forms of energy, solar, hydraulic, and chemical, are old friends and need little further description, we shall discuss some salient points about nuclear energy:

(1) One way to describe the intensity of nuclear energy is to use a common term of the physicists, the *electron-volt*. An electron-volt is the amount of energy required to move an electronic charge a distance corresponding to a change in voltage from 0 to −1 volt. The energy deficiency which binds a valence electron to an atom is of the order of a few electron-volts whereas

the energy deficiency which binds nucleons (protons and neutrons) together to form an atomic nucleus is of the order of 10 million ev per nucleon. Consequently, the energy released per atom in burning fossil fuel is of the order of a few electron-volts, whereas the energy released in nuclear interactions is measured in millions of electron-volts.

Chemical Reaction:

$$2H_2 + O_2 = 2H_2O + 5.92 \text{ ev}$$

$$C + O_2 = CO_2 + 4.17 \text{ ev}$$

Fission Reaction:

$$U^{235} + n \longrightarrow \text{stable nuclei} + xn + 1.65 \times 10^8 \text{ ev (average value)}$$

Fusion Reactions:

(1) $$H^2 + H^2 \longrightarrow He^3 + n + 3.2 \times 10^6 \text{ ev}$$

(2) $$H^2 + H^2 \longrightarrow H^3 + H^1 + 4 \times 10^6 \text{ ev}$$

$$H^3 + H^2 \longrightarrow He^4 + n^1 + 17 \times 10^6 \text{ ev}$$

As there are a great number of possible fission reactions, we shall not make a detailed list. The significant fact is that the average energy released per U^{235} atom is 1.65×10^8 ev. In the fusion of deuterons there are two equally likely outcomes which are given as (1) and (2). In (1), two deuteron atoms are used up, and the energy released is 3.2 mev (million electron-volts). In (2), three deuteron atoms are eventually used up, and the total energy released is 21 mev. Thus the average fusion energy per deuteron atom is

$$\frac{(3.2 \times 10^6 + 21 \times 10^6)}{5} = 4.84 \times 10^6 \text{ ev}$$

In contrast, the kinetic energy of a gas molecule at room temperature is about $\frac{1}{40}$ electron-volt!

(2) The total energy stored in fissionable material is of the order of magnitude of the energy stored in fossil fuel deposits. The available fusion energy is practically inexhaustible, however. By this, we do not mean that every hydrogen atom can be used in a fusion reaction. In fact, scientific evidence is strongly against this [3, 4]. Even if we could duplicate the conditions of extreme temperature and pressure inside the sun for a billion years, only 10% of the ordinary hydrogen nuclei would undergo fusion. About 0.015% of hydrogen, however, is the isotope deuteron or H^2. If we duplicate the sun's condition for only a microsecond with deuteron nuclei, an appreciable number of fusion reactions will take place. Thus fusion with H^2 is foreseeable but with H^1 is next to impossible.

To see the implication of the material cited, let us compare the ratio of fusion energy stored in 1 lb of sea water to the chemical energy stored in 1 lb of coal:

$$\frac{\text{energy/lb H}_2\text{O}}{\text{energy/lb C}} = 0.00015 \cdot \frac{12}{18} \cdot \frac{4.84 \times 10^6 \times 2}{4.17} = 230$$

1-3. EINSTEIN'S $E = mc^2$

Perhaps the most publicized law of natural science is Einstein's $E = mc^2$. It means that neither mass nor energy is conserved by itself, but the two are conserved together, and the exchange rate between them is c^2.

The practical significance of this relation lies in the large exchange rate. If 1 kg of mass can be totally converted, the resulting energy is

$$(3 \times 10^8)^2 \text{ joules} = 25 \text{ billion kwhr}$$

which is more than the total consumption of electricity by the whole world in any one day. Contemporary scientific knowledge, however, indicates that there is no way of totally converting a sizable mass into energy. Even in the most celebrated fusion reactions, only a minute fraction of 1% of the total energy is converted.

Einstein's law is useful in two ways:

1. *It gives a necessary condition for a nuclear reaction to take place.*
   Consider the nuclear reaction:

$$A + B \longrightarrow C + D + Q$$

where A, B, C, and D are nuclear particles and Q is the amount of energy released by the reaction. If the total mass of A and B is greater than the total mass of C and D, Einstein's law at least does not say that the reaction is not possible. If it does take place, a positive amount of energy Q will be released. If the total mass of A and B is less than the total mass of C and D, Q is negative and energy must be supplied to A and B to make the reaction possible. This can be done only at high odds by nuclear bombardments. The reaction does not occur under natural circumstances. For instance, the reaction of a neutron spontaneously decaying into a proton and an electron:

$$n^1 \longrightarrow H^1 + e^- + Q$$

is a possible one because the atomic mass of the neutron is 1.008982 whereas the atomic mass of a hydrogen atom (nucleus together with an electron) is 1.008142. But the reaction of a hydrogen atom becoming a neutron

$$H^1 + e^- \longrightarrow n^1 + Q$$

is impossible.

2. *It allows the energy released in a nuclear reaction to be exactly calculated.*
From Einstein's relation

$$Q = \Delta m \, c^2 \qquad\qquad (1\text{–}1)$$

where the mass difference Δm is the total mass of particles entering a reaction minus the total mass of particles resulting from a reaction.

One important simplification of the above relation is *use of atomic masses instead of the masses of the particles.* For instance, Δm of fusion reaction (1) can be calculated as

$\Delta m = 2 \times$ mass of deuteron atom

$-$ mass of helium^3 atom $-$ mass of neutron

The mass of each deuteron atom includes that of an extra electron. The mass of a helium atom includes that of two extra electrons. Thus the extras are canceled out exactly. In general, the total charges of the nuclei remain unchanged in a reaction without β-decay, and the total number of electrons to make up the atoms does not change. In case an electron is emitted (β^--decay), the emitted electron is exactly what is needed to make up the required extra electron in the new atom. In case a positron is emitted (β^+-decay), the Δm, as calculated from the atomic masses, is too large by exactly the mass of two electrons. As the positron can never last, however, nor should it be allowed to escape, it eventually annihilates an electron and releases the energy $2mc^2$, where m is the mass of an electron. The calculation is again correct as it not only accounts for the initial energy release, but also the subsequent energy release due to annihilation of the positron electron pair.*

As an example, consider the decay reaction

$$Co^{60} \longrightarrow Ni^{60} + e^- + Q$$

The Co atom has 27 electrons whereas the Ni atom has 28. The mass difference between a Co atom and a Ni atom is exactly the same as the

---

* The only exception to the rule is when a nutrino or an antinutrino is emitted. These particles can penetrate great thicknesses of matter without being stopped and they are likely to escape and cause a reduction in the total energy released. In all known reactions, however, they amount to only a small fraction of the total energy released; therefore they do not change the order of magnitude of the latter.

mass difference between a Co nucleus and a Ni nucleus plus an electron. The atomic weights are

$$Co^{60}: \quad 59.95250$$

$$Ni^{60}: \quad 59.94948$$

The energy released per atom is

$$Q = \frac{0.00302 \times 9 \times 10^{16}}{6.0247 \times 10^{26}} = 4.51 \times 10^{-13} \text{ joule}$$

$$= 4.51 \times 10^{-13} \text{ joule} \times \frac{1 \text{ ev}}{1.6021 \times 10^{-19} \text{ joule}}$$

$$= 2.81 \times 10^6 \text{ ev}$$

To get some idea of how radioactive fuel compares with conventional fuel, we calculate the following ratio:

$$\frac{\text{energy/lb } Co^{60}}{\text{energy/lb C}} = \frac{12}{60} \cdot \frac{2.81 \times 10^6}{4.17}$$

$$= 1.35 \times 10^5$$

Thus one pound of Co^{60} is approximately equivalent to 60 tons of carbon in its fuel value.

The isotope Co^{60} has a half-life of $5\frac{1}{4}$ years and is certainly "hot" enough to be used as a fuel. It is not a prime energy source, however, as intensely radioactive materials are not found in nature. These materials would have decayed long since the day of their creation. They can only be manufactured in a rather expensive way in a nuclear reactor.

The advantage of these materials over fission and fusion fuel is the ability to use them without much auxiliary equipment and over a long period of time. In space applications where the space vehicle is very far from the sun and solar cells are no longer economical, radioactive isotopes are the best primary power for instrumentation and communication.

1-4. ENERGY CONVERSION CHART

Figure 1–1 illustrates the various ways of converting different forms of natural energy into electrical energy. The natural energies are listed at the bottom of the chart and the paths leading to electrical energy are shown. The solid-line paths represent conversion processes which have been proved feasible at least experimentally. The fusion processes are represented by

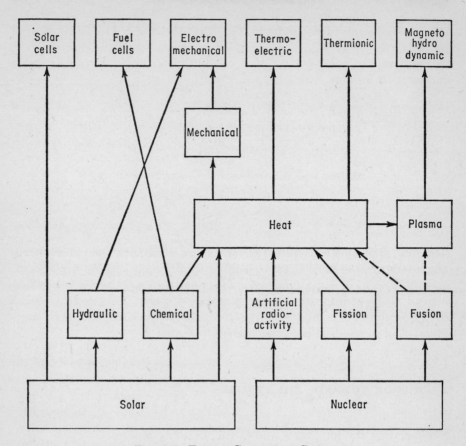

Fig. 1–1. Energy Conversion Chart.

broken lines, as their feasibilities are still in doubt. We know that fusion energy can be released at a tremendous rate, as in the sun's interior or in a hydrogen bomb. We also know that fusion energy can be released in small doses under laboratory-created high-temperature conditions with far more energy put into the process than the energy released. As yet, we do not know whether fusion energy can be released at a moderate, self-sustaining rate so that it can be harnessed and converted into electrical energy. At present, the most exploited paths are

$$\text{fossil fuel} \xrightarrow[\text{turbine}]{\text{steam}} \text{heat} \xrightarrow{\text{generator}} \text{mechanical energy} \xrightarrow{\text{generator}} \text{electrical energy}$$

$$\text{hydraulic energy} \xrightarrow[\text{turbine}]{\text{hydraulic}} \text{mechanical energy} \xrightarrow{\text{generator}} \text{electrical energy}$$

The machines most frequently used to effect the conversions are indicated on top of the links. What method of energy conversion will be used in the future, however, is a big question mark. For instance, if the fusion process can be used we may have

$$\text{nuclear fusion} \xrightarrow{\text{\textit{magnetohydrodynamic generator}}} \text{electrical energy}$$

$$\text{nuclear fusion} \xrightarrow{\text{\textit{thermoelectric or thermionic}}} \text{heat} \longrightarrow \text{electrical energy}$$

$$\text{nuclear fusion} \xrightarrow{\text{\textit{steam turbine}}} \text{heat} \longrightarrow \text{mechanical energy} \xrightarrow{\text{\textit{generator}}} \text{electrical energy}$$

The first path illustrates direct generation of electricity from the plasma (high-temperature ionized gas) resulting from nuclear fusion. The second and third paths illustrate utilization of the heat released by nuclear fusion instead of direct utilization of the plasma. Of course, the two basic ways can also be used in conjunction. It is not yet known which method or combination of methods is most efficient.

1-5. A LOOK TOWARDS THE FUTURE

Summarizing the foregoing, we see the following picture:

(1) The conventional energy source, fossil energy, is rapidly being exhausted and is totally inadequate to meet future needs.

(2) The technology of making use of fission energy is quite well developed, and in all likelihood, fission energy will play a substantial role in the near future. As available fissionable material is limited, however, and its total energy is of the same order of magnitude of the fossil energy, the development of fission energy is not likely to be more than a stepping stone from a long-range viewpoint.

(3) There are two practically inexhaustible and unlimited sources of energy: solar and fusion. The process of converting fusion energy into electrical energy is still not developed. The most efficient process of converting solar energy into electrical energy is the solar cell. It has proved feasible in terms of conversion efficiency, but is too expensive with the present facilities for manufacturing. Another characteristic drawback of solar energy is

that a substantial part of the surface of earth must be covered with conversion devices. The construction and maintenance of such a system is a gigantic task by any standard.

What prediction can we make then from these known facts? It is highly unlikely that technology in power generation will halt at the present state of affairs, and a worldwise program of conservation of resources be instituted. For one thing, the prospect of practically unlimited availability of electric power is too good and valuable to be given up lightly. To a layman, electric power is no more than the utility which energizes electric motors in the factory, and refrigerators, washing machines, and light bulbs at home. But it is far more than that. It is one of the basic cost factors which determine what enterprise or mode of life is feasible or not feasible in an industrial, scientifically enlightened society. For instance, many desert lands can be converted into fertile soil if drinking and irrigation water is available. The method of converting sea water for this purpose is not lacking except for the power cost. Although at the present rate, the methods are too prohibitively expensive for most applications, the balance can be changed if sufficient electric power is available at low cost. As another example, most of us enjoy the freedom offered by an automobile. What if petroleum deposits are used up or nearly used up? Does that mean that in future generations almost everyone must depend on public transportation? The answer is no if there is adequate supply of electric power so that synthetic fuel can be economically made. As a third example, the ultimate factor which distinguishes a high-grade ore from an ore of marginal quality is no other than the cost of electric energy for separating the desired metal from the remaining material. To speak figuratively, an almost unlimited supply of electric power is the magic wand which turns deserts into fertile soil, inert compounds into fuel, and rocks into rich mines. Its potential benefits to mankind cannot be overstated.

Yet the goal of practically unlimited supply of electric power is already within sight. Even if the conversion of fusion energy proves to be a dead-end alley, there is no insurmountable hurdle in the way of developing solar energy. The basic material for making solar cells is silicon, which is literally everywhere on earth. The production and maintenance of solar cells are the kind of processes which adapt readily to automation. In the last analysis, the major cost item, beside human efforts and ingenuity, is again electric energy, of which far less is required in comparison to the total amount generated in the practically unlimited lifetime of a solar cell. It is quite safe to conclude that, in one way or another, the worthwhile goal of a practically unlimited source of electric power can be realized and that it is a task which should prove to be both challenging and rewarding.

1-6. A WORD ABOUT THE PRESENT VOLUME

This volume is concerned mainly with the last link to electric energy listed at the top of the energy-conversion chart except the problem of conversion between electrical energy and mechanical energy. It gives the basic principle as well as an analysis of the important factors which limit the performance of each type of energy converter. As the electromechanical energy-conversion link is the best-developed and analyzed, its inclusion in this volume does not appear necessary.

In subsequent chapters, the mks system of units is used. This system has the advantage of being both consistent and unique, in the sense that there is only one unit for each physical entity. When we write a mathematical symbol to represent a physical quantity *without specifying the unit*, we mean that the appropriate mks unit is used. This cannot be done if we use English units. For instance, if the physical entity is length, the only possible unit in the mks system is the meter but it could be anything in the English unit—the foot, inch, yard, mile, etc. The use of mks units also results in great simplification of the proportionality constants in equations.

A conversion table of mks to cgs and English units and vice versa is given in Appendix A.

REFERENCES

1. Hutcheson, J. A., "Engineering for the Future," *Jour. of Eng. Ed.*, April, 1960, pp. 602–607.

2. Hutcheson, J. A., "Engineering for the Future," *Jour. of Eng. Ed.*, April, 1960, pp. 602–607.

3. Marchak, R. E., "The Energy of Stars," *Scientific American Reader*, pp. 176–84. New York: Simon and Schuster, 1953.

4. Bethe, H. A., "The Hydrogen Bomb II," *Scientific American Reader*, pp. 190–200. New York: Simon and Schuster, 1953.

5. Sproull, R. L., *Modern Physics*, pp. 65–70; 416–35. New York: John Wiley & Sons, 1956.

PROBLEMS

1-1. In the fusion reaction of a pure deuteron gas, the following assumptions are made:

   (a) About 80% of the deuterons are used up in a flash during which time no energy has escaped.

(b) The gas is completely ionized, i.e., none of the electrons is bound to a nucleus, and the released fusion energy is divided alike by all particles present: electrons, neutrons, and various types of nuclei.

Calculate the average energy E per particle. The temperature T of the gas is related to E by

$$E = \tfrac{3}{2}kT$$

Calculate T. The constant k is given as 8.616×10^{-5} ev per degree.

1–2. The atomic mass in kilograms is the mass of N_0 atoms, where N_0 is Avogadro's number 6.0247×10^{26}. The following atomic masses are given

n	1.00898
H^1	1.00814
H^2	2.01474
H^3	3.01700
He^4	4.00387

Use Einstein's equation $E = mc^2$ and calculate the fusion energies released in reaction (2). Does your result check with the figures 4×10^6 ev given (1 ev $= 1.6021 \times 10^{-19}$ joule)?

1–3. Calculate the atomic mass of He^3 from the fusion reaction (1).

1–4. What is the excess molecular mass of C and O_2 together over that of CO_2? To what degree of accuracy do we need to improve the balance in order to detect mass difference in chemical reactions?

CHAPTER TWO

BASIC SCIENCE
OF ENERGY CONVERSION

The first and second laws of thermodynamics are two fundamental laws for all energy-conversion systems. Within the confines of these laws, quantum mechanics and the subsequent development in semiconductors have furnished an important vehicle for the advancement of the methods for energy conversion and materials for effective realization of these methods.

Although the classical thermodynamic theory and the modern quantum theory are thus equally important, engineering work in this area usually requires quantitative and precise application of the former but only qualitative application of the latter. A reader is expected to understand the treatment of the two laws of thermodynamics in Part A thoroughly. An equally thorough understanding of Part B is desirable but not as essential. One may accept the existence of photons, discrete energy states, band structure of solids, Fermi factor, and conduction by electrons and holes as isolated facts and proceed to the later chapters on that basis.

A. THE TWO LAWS OF THERMODYNAMICS

The two laws of thermodynamics are

1. The principle of conservation of energy
2. The principle of non-decrease of entropy

The principle of conservation of energy yields an exact equation for the total energy balance in any energy conversion system; the principle of non-decrease of entropy places a value on the generation or transfer of heat in any energy conversion system. Each principle is as fundamental as the other. Just as we cannot prove the conservation of energy, we cannot *prove* the non-decrease of entropy without assuming an equally fundamental alternative. As entropy is a rather abstract concept, however, it is worthwhile to state the second law in its more intuitive form:

> *It is not possible to transfer heat from a cold body to a hot body without changing something else.*

The foregoing statement was due to Clausius and will be referred to as 2(a). We shall show that 2 follows from 2(a), and vice versa, and introduce the concept of reversibility and entropy in the course of the proof. The significance of the development is that, whereas 2(a) is almost common sense, 2 is so sweeping and significant that many physical laws and design equations of energy conversion systems follow from it.

The first and second laws are then formulated into a systematic method for analyzing energy-conversion devices.

2-1. PRINCIPLE OF CONSERVATION OF ENERGY: THE FIRST LAW OF THERMODYNAMICS

The conversion between mass and energy as discussed in Sec. 1–3 does not occur under ordinary circumstances. The conversion of energy into mass has been known to exist only in laboratory-created high-speed collision processes of isolated particles. Even then, the number of particles involved is very small, and the total energy converted into mass is negligible. The conversion of mass into energy can take place only with specially prepared material which can be regarded as a kind of fuel which liberates energy when it itself is "burned" into "ash." These materials and the devices for utilizing them to generate heat can be readily identified and treated separately as sources of heat. Energy is conserved by itself in the remaining system.

Consider a complex system. The energy stored in the system may consist of

1. Internal energy, such as nuclear, chemical or thermal energy
2. Electrical energy in the form of electromagnetic or electrostatic energy
3. Mechanical energy in the form of kinetic or potential energy

Energy may be imported *into* the system by conducting, convecting, or radiating heat into the system, or by doing work mechanically or electrically upon the system; or it may be exported *from* the system by conducting, convecting, or radiating heat away, or by allowing the system to do the work. Let

U = total internal energy,

ΔQ = net heat transferred *into* the system,

ΔW = net work done by the system,

   = total work done by the system − total work done upon the system.

The principle of conservation of energy states that the increase in internal energy ΔU is related to ΔQ and ΔW by

$$\Delta U = \Delta Q - \Delta W \qquad (2\text{–}1)$$

Since the energy balance should hold for an infinitesmal change,

$$dU = dQ - dW \qquad (2\text{–}2)$$

In other words, the total energy of any system is constant. It is simply converted from one form to another. We shall illustrate the application of Eq. (2–1) and Eq. (2–2) by a few examples:

Example 2–1: A three-phase 440-volt 75-hp induction motor has a full-load line current of 89 amp at 90% power factor, and is cooled by forced air. How much heat is dissipated into the cooling air and the surroundings per second if the motor is to operate at a steady temperature?

SOLUTION: If the motor is to operate at a steady temperature, $\Delta U = 0$, and Eq. (2–1) gives the energy balance in 1 sec as

$\Delta Q = \Delta W$ = mechanical output − electrical input

$\qquad = 75 \times 746$ joules $- 440\ \sqrt{3} \times 89 \times 0.9$ joule

$\qquad = 56,000 - 61,000 = -5,000$ joules

The heat dissipated by the motor in 1 sec is $-\Delta Q = 5,000$ joules.

Before giving Ex. 2–2 and Ex. 2–3, we shall review briefly the properties of the ideal gas. A well-known physical law is the ideal gas law:

$$pV = mRT \qquad (2\text{–}3)$$

where p = pressure in newton/m²,

V = volume in m³,

T = temperature in °K,

R = a universal constant, 8310 joules/°K,

m = amount of gas in kilogram molecular weight. For instance, the molecular weight of O_2 is $16 \times 2 = 32$. If the mass of O_2 under consideration is 2 kg, then $m = 2$ kg/32 kg = 0.0625. The unit of kilogram molecular weight is abbreviated as kilogram mole.

Another well-known fact about the ideal gas is that its internal energy U is a function of temperature only.

There are two types of specific heat: C_V is the specific heat of a kilogram mole of gas at constant volume, and C_p is that at constant pressure. Referring to Fig. 2–1, if the piston is held fixed and heat is applied to the gas through the walls, then the temperature rise ΔT is given by

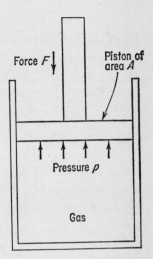

Force F Piston of area A

Pressure p

Gas

$$[\Delta Q]_{V=\text{constant}} = mC_V \,\Delta T \qquad (2\text{–}4)$$

If the pressure is kept constant by applying a constant force

$$F = pA \qquad (2\text{–}5)$$

against the piston, which is otherwise allowed to move freely, then

Fig. 2–1. A Piston and Cylinder Unit.

$$[\Delta Q]_{p=\text{constant}} = mC_p \,\Delta T \qquad (2\text{–}6)$$

Example 2–2: Show that

$$C_p = C_V + R \qquad (2\text{–}7)$$

Solution: Consider the case when the piston is held fixed, $\Delta W = 0$. Equations (2–1) and (2–4) give

$$\Delta U = mC_V \,\Delta T \qquad (2\text{–}8)$$

Now consider the case when a force F is applied to the piston, which is balanced by the pressure from inside, and the piston is free to move. The work done by the gas is

$$\Delta W = F \,\Delta x = \frac{F}{A} \cdot A \,\Delta x = p \,\Delta V \qquad (2\text{–}9)$$

As the internal energy U is a function of temperature only, Eq. (2-8) is still valid. Equation (2-1) gives

$$\Delta Q = mC_V \, \Delta T + p \, \Delta V \qquad (2\text{-}10)$$

For infinitesimal change, Eq. (2-10) is true whether p is constant or not. If p remains constant, Eq. (2-3) gives

$$p \, \Delta V = mR \, \Delta T \qquad (2\text{-}11)$$

Substituting Eq. (2-6) and Eq. (2-11) into Eq. (2-10) gives

$$mC_p \, \Delta T = mC_V \, \Delta T + mR \, \Delta T$$

Dividing the foregoing equation by $m \, \Delta T$ gives Eq. (2-7).

Example 2-3: An *adiabatic process* means that there is no heat exchange between the system under consideration and its surroundings: $\Delta Q = 0$. In Fig. 2-1, this would be true if both the cylinder and the piston were thermally insulated. Show that for adiabatic compression or expansion of a gas, the following equations are true:

$$pV^\gamma = \text{constant}_1 \qquad (2\text{-}12)$$

$$TV^{\gamma-1} = \text{constant}_2 \qquad (2\text{-}13)$$

where γ is used to denote the ratio C_p/C_V. Subscripts 1 and 2 mean that these constants are different. They will not be written explicitly in the applications of these equations in later sections.

SOLUTION: From Eq. (2-7)

$$\frac{R}{C_V} = \frac{C_p - C_V}{C_V} = \gamma - 1$$

Setting $\Delta Q = 0$ in Eq. (2-10) and substituting mRT/V for p gives

$$mC_V \, dT + mRT \, \frac{dV}{V} = 0$$

The letter d is used instead of Δ, since, with p varying, Eq. (2-10) is valid only for an infinitesimal change. Dividing the foregoing equation by $mC_V T$ and substituting $\gamma - 1$ for R/C_V give

$$\frac{dT}{T} + (\gamma - 1) \frac{dV}{V} = 0$$

Integrating the preceding equation gives Eq. (2-13). Substituting pV/mR for T in Eq. (2-13) gives

$$pV^\gamma = \frac{\text{constant}_2}{mR} = \text{constant}_1$$

2-2. HEAT CONTENT AND ENTHALPY

When a piece of material is being heated or cooled, it is usually not confined to a fixed volume. More frequently, a constant pressure is applied to the material. With p constant, the work done by thermal expansion of the material is

$$\Delta W = p \, \Delta V = \Delta(pV)$$

Equation (2-1) becomes

$$\Delta Q = \Delta(U + pV) \tag{2-14}$$

The quantity $U + pV$ is called the *enthalpy* and also *heat content* of the material. It is usually denoted by the symbol H:

$$H \equiv U + pV \tag{2-15}$$

If p is not constant, Eq. (2-2) gives

$$dQ = dU + p \, dV = dH - V \, dp$$

Consider a process which takes the working material from State 1 with pressure p_1 and volume V_1 to State 2 with pressure p_2 and volume V_2. The heat absorbed by the material is obtained by integrating the foregoing expression:

$$\Delta Q = \Delta H - \int_1^2 V \, dp$$

In general $\Delta Q \neq \Delta H$. If p increases throughout the process, $\Delta Q < \Delta H$. If p decreases throughout the process, $\Delta Q > \Delta H$. We see that H represents the heat content literally only in the special case of constant pressure processes. In general, the increase of H of a material is not equal to the heat it absorbed.

What then is the real significance of H? Why is Q not defined as the heat content?

Actually, given the initial and final states, the value of ΔQ is not known at all. The heat absorbed usually depends on the process or path. To illustrate this point consider an ideal gas initially at a pressure p_1 and occupying a volume V_1. The gas is heated until it finally reaches a pressure p_2 and volume V_2:

$$p_2 = 2p_1$$

$$V_2 = 2V_1$$

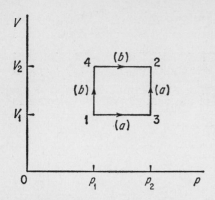

Fig. 2-2. A VOLUME VERSUS
PRESSURE DIAGRAM.

On the p-V diagram of Fig. 2-2, only the initial and final points are fixed, and there are many ways of reaching the final point from the initial point. For instance, we may fix the position of the piston of Fig. 2-1, heat the gas at constant volume until its pressure reaches p_2, and then keep the force in balance with p_2 and heat the gas at constant pressure until its volume reaches V_2 as illustrated by path (a). Alternatively we may heat the gas at constant pressure first and then at constant volume as illustrated by path (b).

At the final state, the temperature T_2 is

$$T_2 = \frac{p_2 V_2}{mR} = \frac{4 p_1 V_1}{mR} = 4 T_1$$

At the middle points, the temperatures T_3 and T_4 are

$$T_3 = T_4 = 2 T_1$$

Therefore,

$$(\Delta Q)_a = mC_V(2T_1 - T_1) + mC_p(4T_1 - 2T_1)$$

$$= (C_V T_1 + 2C_p T_1)m = (3C_V + 2R)mT_1$$

$$(\Delta Q)_b = mC_p(2T_1 - T_1) + mC_V(4T_1 - 2T_1)$$

$$= (3C_V + R)mT_1$$

$$\Delta H = \Delta(mC_V T + mRT) = m(C_V + R)\,\Delta T$$

$$= 3m(C_V + R)T_1$$

The preceding calculations illustrate that the heat absorbed by the gas depends on the path it takes to reach the final state and is not equal to the increase in H.

There are two types of thermodynamic variables: a *variable of the state* depends *only* on the state or condition the material is in; a *variable of the path* depends not only on the state of the material but also on how that state is reached. Among the thermodynamic variables which have been discussed, p, V, T, U, and H are variables of the state, and Q is a variable of the path.

For a homogeneous material there are two independent variables of the state. The other variables of the state can be expressed as functions of these two. The properties of the material are specified by these functions. The choice of the two independent variables is not unique, e.g., p, V; p, T; etc.

For example, the variables p and V of an ideal gas can be selected as the independent ones. Then,

$$T = \frac{pV}{mR}$$

$$U = mC_V T = \frac{C_V pV}{R} = \frac{pV}{\gamma - 1}$$

$$H = U + pV = \frac{\gamma pV}{\gamma - 1}$$

Alternatively, p and H may be selected

$$V = \frac{(\gamma - 1)H}{\gamma p}$$

$$U = \frac{H}{\gamma}$$

$$T = \frac{(\gamma - 1)H}{\gamma mR}$$

The condition or property of a material can only be specified by variables of state.

Keeping the foregoing in mind, we see that the term *heat content* is very misleading: Its literal meaning is the heat contained in a material. Since it describes a condition of the material, it should be a variable of the state. On the other hand, if a material absorbs an amount of heat ΔQ; then, in plain English, its heat content should be increased by ΔQ. But since ΔQ depends on the path, *heat content* becomes necessarily a variable of the path. The difficulty lies in that a material has no property which is literally a heat content, and the word "enthalpy" was coined to avoid this difficulty.

We may say that the enthalpy, H, is a variable of the state which can be identified literally as the heat content in the special case of processes with constant pressure. Being a variable of the state, however, its significance is not limited to this particular type of processes. Other significances of H will be discussed later, in connection with flow processes in Chapter 5 and in connection with free energies in Chapter 7.

As the terms *heat content* and *enthalpy* are used synonymously in the literature, we shall continue that usage; both terms mean H as defined in Eq. (2–15).

2-3. ORDERLY AND DISORDERLY ENERGY

As discussed in the preceding section, energy may take many forms, with different attributes. What really counts in any conversion process is whether the energy is in an orderly or a disorderly form. The kinetic and potential energies of a moving body are orderly forms of energy: The kinetic energy is due to the coordinated motion of all the molecules with the same average velocity in the same direction. The potential energy is owing to the vantage position taken by the molecules, or displacements of the molecules from their normal positions. Similarly, the electrostatic energy is due to a gathering of charged particles of the same polarity, and the electromagnetic energy of an electric current in a coil is owing to the coordinated drift of charge carriers which induces a magnetic field which in turn tends to sustain the continued drift of the charge carriers.

In contrast to the forms of energy just cited, the thermal energy or heat is due to the random movements of molecules in a completely disorderly fashion. The motion of an individual molecule is not related to any other molecule, and the average velocity in any direction is zero.

In between these two extremes, chemical energy may be considered partially orderly.

Our experience shows that orderly energy can be readily converted into disorderly energy. For instance, mechanical and electrical energies can be converted into heat by friction and i^2R loss. Orderly energies can also be readily converted into one another. But we have no machine which draws heat steadily from its surroundings and converts it into motion or electrical energy. Furthermore, Statement 2(a) is the same as saying that disorderly energy at a lower temperature cannot be converted into disorderly energy at a higher temperature. Thus there are natural limitations on the conversion of disorderly energy into orderly energy or into disorderly energy at a different temperature.

In terms of energy conversion, the principle of conservation of energy sets up an equation between the ingredients entering a conversion process and the products of that process. But another principle is needed to indicate the direction in which the conversion may go. Sometimes, it is possible in one direction only; sometimes, it is possible both ways. In order for an energy conversion process to work, the direction it takes must be a possible one. If both directions are possible, then the new principle must be able to indicate the factors by which we can control the direction of the conversion process.

The discovery of such a powerful principle of immense practical value from the relatively insignificant clue of Statement 2(a) was made by a few scientists early in the nineteenth century. This second principle, or second law of thermodynamics, was contained implicitly in the work of Carnot in 1824, but it was first clearly stated by Clausius and Lord Kelvin independently in 1850 and 1851, respectively. The reasoning of these scientific sleuths beggars the best detective stories ever written, and in all likelihood, those not yet written. In the following sections, we shall describe the essence of this superb deductive process and spice it with some engineering flavor.

We begin by introducing a few useful terms.

2-4. THE HEAT ENGINE, REFRIGERATION ENGINE, THERMAL EFFICIENCY, AND THERMAL EXCHANGE RATIO

Man-made engines usually utilize a certain tendency of nature in order to do some work or to reverse the natural process by putting some work into it. An outstanding example is illustrated in Fig. 2-3. There is a heat reservoir R_1 at temperature T_1 and a heat reservoir R_2 at a lower temperature T_2. In Fig. 2-3(a), instead of allowing heat to transfer freely from R_1 to R_2, we use a heat engine to exploit this process in order to produce some useful work W'. Thus the heat Q_1' taken from R_1 is no longer equal to the heat Q_2' delivered to R_2. From the conservation of energy, we have

$$W' = Q_1' - Q_2' \qquad (2\text{-}16)$$

An example of heat engine is the steam turbine. R_1 is the boiler; R_2 is the surrounding atmosphere or cooling water which absorbs heat from the condensing steam. Not so obvious an example is the internal combustion engine. Here, the ignition of the fuel supplies Q_1' and takes the place of R_1. We may regard T_1 as the gas temperature at the completion of ignition.

In Fig. 2-3(b), the natural process is reversed by applying an external work W'' to the system. Heat Q_2'' is taken from R_2 by the refrigeration engine, and heat Q_1'' is delivered to R_1. Because of conservation of energy,

$$Q_1'' = Q_2'' + W'' \qquad (2\text{-}17)$$

The air-conditioner is an example of a refrigeration engine. The air-conditioned space is R_2; the external atmosphere or cooling water is R_1.

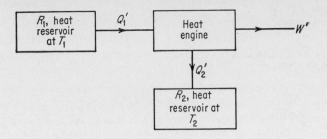

(*a*) Heat engine

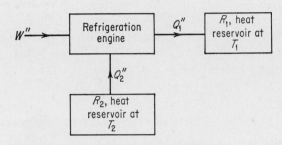

(*b*) Refrigeration engine

Fig. 2–3. Block Diagram of Thermodynamic Engines.

In the previous discussions as well as the discussions to follow, it is assumed that the heat and refrigeration engines are operating under steady state condition. The engine condition, which includes temperatures at various points, working material, etc., remains unchanged before and after the energy-conversion operation. Thus the only changes which have taken place are the heat exchanges at the reservoirs and the work W either absorbed or delivered.

A measure of the effectiveness of a machine is the ratio:

$$\frac{\text{useful output}}{\text{total input}}$$

For a heat engine, the useful output is mechanical work, W', and the total input is thermal energy, Q'_1, at temperature T_1. Thus,

$$\eta = \frac{W'}{Q'_1} = \frac{W'}{W' + Q'_2} \tag{2–18}$$

In Eq. (2–18), η is the usual definition of *thermal efficiency* for a heat engine. On the other hand, for a refrigeration engine, the useful output is a reduction in thermal energy, Q_2'', and the input is the mechanical work, W''. The ratio which interests a designer is the coefficient of performance, C:

$$C = \frac{Q_2''}{W''} \tag{2-19}$$

It should be realized that C can be greater than unity and often is very much greater than unity.

Another important ratio is the thermal exchange ratio, ρ. For any engine, ρ is defined as the ratio of thermal energies transferred at the lower and higher temperatures:

$$\rho' = \frac{Q_2'}{Q_1'} \qquad \rho'' = \frac{Q_2''}{Q_1''} \tag{2-20}$$

From the definitions in Eq. (2–18), Eq. (2–19), and Eq. (2–20) and from Eq. (2–16) and Eq. (2–17), we obtain

$$\eta = \frac{Q_1' - Q_2'}{Q_1'} = 1 - \rho' \tag{2-21}$$

$$C = \frac{Q_2''}{Q_1'' - Q_2''} = \frac{\rho''}{1 - \rho''} \tag{2-22}$$

As mentioned previously, the following is one important condition in measuring the quantities Q_1', Q_1'', Q_2', Q_2'', W', and W'':

There is no change in the engine itself at the end of the operating period from what it has been at the beginning of the operating period.

Otherwise, the measurement would be meaningless because we do not know whether the changed engine will have the same operating efficiency as before. To drive home the significance of this condition, let us consider a radical case. We may put a d-c motor and a storage battery in a black box and call it *an engine*. Heat can be transferred in and out of the black box and work is done by the black box. To all appearances, it is an engine. At the end of the operating period, however, the engine cannot be the same as before because some electricity has been drained from the storage battery. With the very general description we have, we need the condition of no change to exclude all hoax engines. Otherwise, we can say nothing of the engine performance.

From a more practical standpoint, all engines arrive at a steady state condition of operation after some initial operating period. The test procedures usually call for establishing the steady state operating condition first before making any performance measurements. Most engines operate cyclically, and to be rigorously correct, one must require that the measurements be made over an integral number of cycles. As the measuring period usually contains a large number of operating cycles, however, this last condition is generally ignored in practice.

2-5. REVERSIBLE AND IRREVERSIBLE ENGINES

An engine is called *reversible* if it satisfies two conditions:

1. It can operate both as a heat engine and as a refrigeration engine.
2. It has the same thermal exchange ratio ρ for both directions of operation between the same temperatures T_1 and T_2.

The foregoing is the thermodynamical definition of a reversible engine. It is far more strict than the term *reversible engine* in common usage. The latter implies only Condition 1. If an engine satisfies Condition 1 but not Condition 2, it is *irreversible* in the thermodynamical sense. In this book, we use the term *reversible engine* in its thermodynamical sense and refer to an engine which satisfies Condition 1 only as *basically reversible*, but not *reversible*.

The concept that *heat cannot be transferred from a cold body (at a lower temperature) to a hot body (at a higher temperature) while leaving everything else unchanged* leads to a very natural classification of reversible and irreversible engines. To see this, we shall use this concept as a postulate and prove three propositions from it:

Proposition 1. The thermal exchange ratio for any refrigeration engine is smaller than, or equal to, the thermal exchange ratio for any heat engine which operates between the same temperatures T_1 *and* T_2. *In other words:*

$$\rho'' \leq \rho' \qquad (2-23)$$

To prove the preceding proposition, let us consider any refrigeration engine and any heat engine operating between the same temperatures T_1 and T_2. We can connect the two engines as shown in Fig. 2–4 and make the heat engine run just long enough to supply the mechanical energy taken by the refrigeration engine:

$$W'' = W' = W \qquad (2-24)$$

Thermal energy Q_1'' is transferred from the refrigeration engine into R_1 and thermal energy Q_1' is transferred from R_1 to the heat engine. Therefore, the net heat transferred *into* R_1 is

$$Q_1'' - Q_1'$$

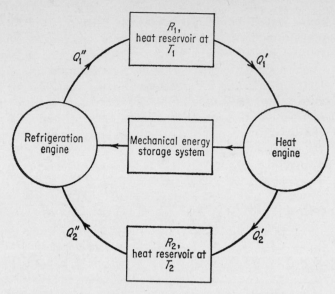

Fig. 2-4. A Hypothetical Arrangement of Engines for Proving Proposition 1.

Thermal energy Q_2'' is transferred from R_2 into the refrigeration engine and thermal energy Q_2' is transferred from the heat engine into R_2. Therefore, the net heat transferred *from* R_2 is

$$Q_2'' - Q_2'$$

Since $W'' = W' = W$, it follows that $Q_1'' - Q_2'' = Q_1' - Q_2'$, and we may define a Q as

$$Q \equiv Q_1'' - Q_1' = Q_2'' - Q_2' \tag{2-25}$$

If $\rho'' > \rho'$, we can prove a contradiction as follows:

$$\frac{Q_2''}{Q_1''} > \frac{Q_2'}{Q_1'} \tag{2-26}$$

$$1 - \frac{Q_2''}{Q_1''} < 1 - \frac{Q_2'}{Q_1'} \tag{2-27}$$

$$\frac{W}{Q_1''} < \frac{W}{Q_1'} \tag{2-28}$$

Therefore, $Q_1'' > Q_1'$ and

$$Q = Q_1'' - Q_1' > 0 \tag{2-29}$$

In other words, a positive quantity of heat Q is transferred from a low-temperature reservoir R_2 to a higher-temperature reservoir R_1. The engines have not changed as discussed in Sec. 2–4. The mechanical energy storage system has not changed, since the same W is transferred into, and taken out of, it. The *only* change is the transfer of heat Q from the cold reservoir R_2 to the hot reservoir R_1. As this is in clear contradiction with our postulate (a heat reservoir is a special case of a body with infinite thermal capacity), the assumption of $\rho'' > \rho'$ cannot be correct. On the other hand, if $\rho'' \leq \rho'$, the same steps Eq. (2–26) to Eq. (2–29) lead to $Q \leq 0$. In other words, a positive quantity of heat $-Q$ is transferred from R_1 to R_2. This is allowable by our postulate. Thus we have proved Proposition 1.

Proposition 2. *For any heat engine, refrigeration engine, and reversible engine operating between the same temperatures* T_1 *and* T_2, *the following inequalities are valid:*

$$\rho'' \leq \rho \leq \rho' \qquad (2\text{–}30)$$

The proof of Eq. (2–30) is straightforward: We first operate the reversible engine as a heat engine, and Proposition 1 gives

$$\rho'' \leq \rho \qquad (2\text{–}31)$$

We then operate the reversible engine as a refrigeration engine, and Proposition 1 gives

$$\rho \leq \rho' \qquad (2\text{–}32)$$

Combining Eq. (2–31) and Eq. (2–32) gives (2–30).

Proposition 3. *The thermal exchange ratio for all reversible engines operating between* T_1 *and* T_2 *are exactly the same. The ratio is a function of* T_1 *and* T_2 *only:*

$$\rho = \rho(T_1, T_2) \qquad (2\text{–}33)$$

To prove the foregoing assertion, let us consider *any* two reversible engines A and B with thermal exchange ratios ρ_a and ρ_b. First, A is operated as a heat engine and B is operated as a refrigeration engine. Proposition 1 gives

$$\rho_b \leq \rho_a$$

Now let A be operated as a refrigeration engine and B be operated as a heat engine:

$$\rho_a \leq \rho_b$$

Therefore, the only possible relation is

$$\rho_a = \rho_b \qquad (2\text{–}34)$$

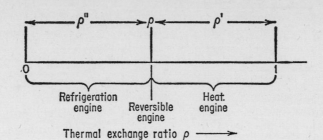

Fig. 2-5. LINE DIAGRAM CHARACTERIZATION OF ENGINES IN TERMS OF THERMAL EXCHANGE RATIO.

All three propositions can be expressed in a one-dimensional graph as shown in Fig. 2-5. Values of ρ are plotted increasing to the right. For given operating temperatures, *only* one value on the graph corresponds to the reversible engine. All values to the left describe the refrigeration engine; all values to the right describe the heat engine.

In conclusion there are two important deductions from the three propositions:

(1) The thermal efficiency η_r and coefficient of performance C_r of a reversible engine are upper limits of η and C of engines operating between the same temperatures T_1 and T_2. This is easy to prove. From $\rho \leq \rho'$, it follows

$$1 - \rho \geq 1 - \rho'$$

Therefore,

$$\eta_r = 1 - \rho \geq \eta \tag{2-35}$$

From $\rho'' \leq \rho$, it follows

$$\frac{\rho}{1 - \rho} = \frac{1}{1 - \rho} - 1 \geq \frac{1}{1 - \rho''} - 1$$

Therefore,

$$C_r \geq C \tag{2-36}$$

(2) Since the thermal exchange ratio for all reversible engines is the same, we can determine its value as well as η_r and C_r by studying *any special case* of a reversible engine. The one we shall study is the Carnot engine as described in subsequent sections.

2-6. THE CARNOT CYCLE

The Carnot cycle is an idealized process which shows one way of converting heat into mechanical energy, and vice versa. Its operation can be explained

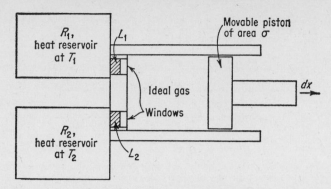

Fig. 2–6. THE CARNOT ENGINE.

with reference to Fig. 2–6 (the Carnot heat engine). A cylinder is completely heat-insulated except for two windows in the back and is filled with ideal gas originally at a high temperature T_1 or rather below T_1 by a negligible amount. The movable piston is linked to a mechanical system which exerts a force on the piston just about in balance with the pressure inside at all times. The force varies as p varies. At the two windows, free thermal exchanges with the two heat reservoirs are possible when we remove the lids L_1 and L_2, but the gas molecules cannot go through these windows. When replaced, the lids L_1 and L_2 serve to heat-insulate the ideal gas completely from the heat reservoirs R_1 and R_2 respectively. We assume that the work required in removing and replacing the lids is negligible, since they can be made to slide with negligible friction.

The operation of the Carnot heat engine can be illustrated by the p-V diagram of Fig. 2–7. It represents the instantaneous pressure

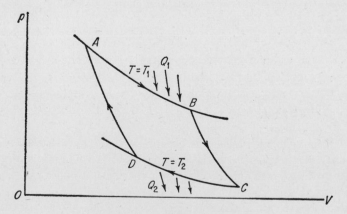

Fig. 2–7. THE CARNOT CYCLE.

versus volume curve during the life history of one cycle. There are the following four phases of operation:

(1) L_1 is removed and the gas expands at constant temperature T_1 from A to B. The work done by the gas on the mechanical system is

$$dW = F\,dx = p\sigma\,dx = p\,dV \qquad (2\text{-}37)$$

$$W_{A\to B} = \int_A^B p\,dV = \int_A^B \frac{mRT_1}{V}\,dV = mRT_1 \log \frac{V}{V_A} \qquad (2\text{-}38)$$

Here we use the subscript to indicate the operating point in Fig. 2-7: V_B is the volume at point B; p_A is the pressure at point A; and $W_{A\to B}$ is the work done by the gas in expanding from A to B, etc. Since temperature remains constant, U does not change, and Eq. (2-1) gives

$$0 = \Delta Q - \Delta W$$

ΔQ is the total heat or thermal energy conducted from reservoir R_1 to the ideal gas in the first phase of the operation, and it will be denoted as Q_1. ΔW is the amount of work $W_{A\to B}$ done by the Carnot engine on the external system. Therefore,

$$Q_1 = W_{A\to B} = mRT_1 \log \frac{V_B}{V_A} \qquad (2\text{-}39)$$

The expansion (or compression) of gas at constant temperature is called *isothermal expansion* (or *compression*).

(2) L_1 is replaced and the gas is completely thermal-insulated from its surroundings. The gas is allowed to continue its expansion adiabatically from B to C. During this phase of the operation, the work done by the gas is obtained from a loss of its internal energy. As $dQ = 0$, Eq. (2-1) gives

$$dU = -p\,dV \qquad (2\text{-}40)$$

From Eq. (2-8), we have an expression for the work done by the gas during this phase:

$$W_{B\to C} = \int_B^C p\,dV = -\int_B^C dU = mC_V(T_1 - T_2) \qquad (2\text{-}41)$$

(3) L_2 is removed, and the gas is compressed by the mechanical system from C to D at a temperature higher than T_2 by a negligible amount. The work done by the mechanical system on the Carnot engine is

$$-W_{C\to D} = -\int_C^D p\,dV = mRT_2 \log \frac{V_C}{V_D} \qquad (2\text{-}42)$$

As the temperature does not change, $\Delta U = 0$. The thermal energy conducted to the heat reservoir R_2 is

$$Q_2 = -W_{C \to D} = mRT_2 \log \frac{V_C}{V_D} \tag{2-43}$$

(4) L_2 is replaced, and the gas is again under complete thermal isolation. The gas is compressed by the mechanical system from D to A. As $\Delta Q = 0$, the work done by the external system to compress the gas is equal to its increase in internal energy

$$-W_{D \to A} = U_A - U_D = mC_V(T_1 - T_2)$$

Now we make a resume of the complete cycle:

1. The gas is returned to its original state and there is no change in the gas or Carnot engine.
2. The thermal energy in reservoir R_1 is reduced by an amount Q_1.
3. The thermal energy in reservoir R_2 is increased by an amount Q_2.
4. The net total work done by the Carnot engine on the mechanical system is

$$W_{A \to B} + W_{B \to C} + W_{C \to D} + W_{D \to A} = Q_1 - Q_2$$

At least theoretically, this work could be stored in a mechanical system as increased kinetic energy, if additional elements were connected to the piston.

Since the changes from B to C and from D to A are both adiabatic, we have, from Eq. (2-13),

$$T_1^{1/(\gamma-1)} V_B = T_2^{1/(\gamma-1)} V_C$$

$$T_1^{1/(\gamma-1)} V_A = T_2^{1/(\gamma-1)} V_D$$

Consequently,

$$\frac{V_B}{V_A} = \frac{V_C}{V_D} \tag{2-44}$$

Equations (2-39), (2-43), and (2-44) give

$$\frac{Q_2}{Q_1} = \frac{T_2}{T_1} \tag{2-45}$$

The Carnot cycle as just described can be operated in reverse as follows:

1. Adiabatic expansion from A to D
2. Isothermal expansion from D to C
3. Adiabatic compression from C to B
4. Isothermal compression from B to A

Obviously the net effects are precisely the opposite in sign to that of the direct Carnot cycle, namely:

1. The gas is returned to its original state and there is no change in the Carnot engine.
2. The thermal energy in reservoir R_1 is *increased* by an amount Q_1.
3. The thermal energy in reservoir R_2 is *decreased* by an amount $Q_2 = Q_1 T_2 / T_1$.
4. The net total work done *by the mechanical system* is $Q_1 - Q_2 = Q_1(1 - T_2/T_1)$.

The reversed Carnot cycle is a refrigeration process. Heat Q_2 is taken away from a reservoir at temperature T_2 and transferred to a reservoir at higher temperature T_1. In order to accomplish this, mechanical work of the amount $Q_1 - Q_2$ has to be applied to the system, increasing the total heat transferred to the reservoir at the higher temperature T_1 to Q_1.

In summary, we have deduced the following:

There exists a reversible process (Carnot cycle) which converts thermal energy Q_1 *at temperature* T_1 *partly into mechanical work* $W = Q_1(1 - T_2/T_1)$, *and partly into thermal energy* $Q_2 = Q_1 T_2 / T_1$ *at a lower temperature* T_2; *and vice versa.*

From the foregoing statement and from Proposition 3 of Sec. 2–5, the thermal exchange ratio of reversible engines is found to be

$$\rho(T_1, T_2) = \frac{T_2}{T_1} \tag{2-46}$$

Equations (2–35), (2–36), and (2–46) can be used to set upper limits for thermal efficiency and coefficient of performance for *any* engine.

Example 2–4: A steam turbine has an entering steam temperature of 800°C and a condensing temperature of 70°C. What is its maximum possible thermal efficiency?

SOLUTION: Equation (2–35) expresses that the upper limit to thermal efficiency is the Carnot efficiency

$$\eta \leq \eta_r = 1 - \frac{T_2}{T_1} = 1 - \frac{70 + 273}{800 + 273} = 0.68$$

Example 2–5: An air-conditioner has the following temperature data:

Outdoor temperature $= 40°C$

Indoor temperature $= 20°C$

Condensing coil temperature $= 57°C$

Evaporating coil temperature $= 7°C$

What is the maximum possible coefficient of performance for the present machine? For any machine under the same indoor-outdoor temperature condition?

SOLUTION: Equation (2-36) gives

$$C \leq C_r = \frac{T_2}{T_1 - T_2}$$

For a refrigeration machine, Q_2'' is absorbed at the evaporation coil temperature and Q_1'' is dissipated at the condensing coil temperature. For the present machine, $T_1 = 57°C$ and $T_2 = 7°C$.

$$C \leq \frac{7 + 273}{57 - 7} = 5.6$$

For any machine, if cost is not a consideration, there is no reason why the evaporating coil temperature should be much below $20°C$, and condensing coil temperature much above $40°C$. The best possible C is obtained with $T_1 = 40°C$, and $T_2 = 20°C$. Therefore,

$$C \leq \frac{20 + 273}{40 - 20} = 14.6$$

2-7. ENTROPY, PROOF OF THE SECOND LAW

With the help of Eq. (2-46), Proposition 2, Sec. 2-5 can be written as

$$\frac{Q_2''}{Q_1''} \leq \frac{T_2}{T_1} \leq \frac{Q_2'}{Q_1'}$$

Therefore, we have for a heat engine

$$\frac{Q_2'}{T_2} \geq \frac{Q_1'}{T_1} \tag{2-47}$$

and for a refrigeration engine

$$\frac{Q_2''}{T_2} \leq \frac{Q_1''}{T_1} \tag{2-48}$$

Equations (2-47) and (2-48) can be written in a more general form. So far, we have used the capital letter Q of various forms to represent *positive* amounts of heat transferred in various cases. Now we use the lower-case letter q_i to be both positive and negative. A negative q_i means that heat q_i is taken from R_i. Equation (2–47) can be written as

$$\frac{q_2}{T_2} \geq \frac{-q_1}{T_1}$$

Equation (2–48) can be written as

$$\frac{q_1}{T_1} \geq \frac{-q_2}{T_2}$$

In both cases, we can write

$$\frac{q_1}{T_1} + \frac{q_2}{T_2} \geq 0 \qquad (2\text{–}49)$$

Sometimes, a heat engine may operate in conjunction with more than two heat reservoirs. We can construct a plural number of Carnot cycles to operate in reverse between these reservoirs so that the net work, as well as the total heat transfer for each reservoir, vanishes except for R_1 and R_2. The same arguments lead to

$$\sum_i \frac{q_i}{T_i} \geq 0 \qquad (2\text{–}50)$$

Here the summation over i is to include all heat reservoirs.

We define entropy:

A quantity associated with a system which increases by an amount q/T *whenever thermal energy* q *is transferred to the system or part thereof, and* T *is the temperature of the part of the system to which heat is transferred and at the time of heat transfer:*

$$\Delta S = \sum_i \frac{q_i}{T_i} \qquad (2\text{–}51)$$

A physical system is *closed* if there is no transfer of energy of whatever form between any component of the system and the external world. The heat engine, its load, and the reservoirs constitute such a system. Equations (2–50) and (2–51) give

$$\Delta S \geq 0 \qquad (2\text{–}52)$$

for a closed physical system. The relation is quite general, as we have assumed nothing about the heat engine except that energy is conserved. The second law of thermodynamics can be stated as:

The entropy of a closed physical system never decreases.

A corollary to the second law is

For a reversible process the total entropy is not changed.

This is easy to prove. For a reversible process,

$$\sum_i \frac{q_i}{T_i} \geq 0$$

$$-\sum_i \frac{q_i}{T_i} \geq 0$$

Therefore,

$$\sum_i \frac{q_i}{T_i} = 0$$

The foregoing presentation gives the definition of entropy and the second law in essence. Although it is a simple concept, it is by no means easy to grasp and apply. We shall discuss a few crucial points in detail in the subsequent section.

One noteworthy point about the second law is that it imposes a condition on the thermal energies transferred to, and from, the various reservoirs. Nothing is said about the work done by the engine or on the engine. Owing to conservation of energy, however, the condition on thermal exchange automatically sets a limit on the mechanical energy produced or expended.

Another way of stating the preceding point is that there is no entropy associated with mechanical energy itself. Only when such energy is dissipated into heat is entropy generated.

2-8. FURTHER REMARKS ON REVERSIBLE PROCESS AND ENTROPY

To begin with, we shall look at the word "reversible" more closely. The conduction of heat from A to B is reversible if A and B are of the same temperature. Obviously, if A and B are of exactly the same temperature, no conduction of heat from A to B can occur. But as long as A is slightly hotter, say, by one-millionth of a degree, and given sufficient time, any finite amount of heat can be conducted from A to B.

Another example is the expansion or compression of a gas. To simplify matters, let it be assumed that the piston of Fig. 2–1 is frictionless and inertialess. The expansion or compression is reversible if $F = pA$. If the gas is to follow the movement of the piston, however, it must have an average drift velocity in the direction of movement of the piston. A slight unbalance between F and pA is necessary to give an average acceleration to the gas molecules so that the required drift can be developed, but any appreciable unbalance would cause the process to be irreversible. To illustrate the point, let us take an extreme case in which the piston is suddenly drawn back a certain distance so fast that a vacuum is temporarily created in the space left behind. As there is no force opposing the movement of the molecules, an appreciable average velocity will be developed on the molecules. These molecules collide eventually with the piston which, by then, has stopped; they are bounced back and then collide with one another until the molecular movements become completely random again. The process cannot be reversed, since it will now take external work to force the molecules back to their original volume and no work has been delivered during the sudden expansion process.

In summary, we may describe a reversible process as a *hypothetical* process in which complete balance (in temperature, pressure, etc.,) is required at every stage.

Now we shall bring our concept of entropy into sharper focus. In Sec. 2-7, we have defined the increase in entropy of a system as

$$\Delta S = \sum_i \frac{q_i}{T_i}$$

This is satisfactory as long as we know all the exchanges of heat that have taken place. Our knowledge, however, is usually incomplete. Typical cases of what we may know are

1. *All the transfers of heat of the system with the external world but not the internal processes*

Would it still be true to say:

$$\Delta S \overset{?}{=} \left(\sum_i \frac{q_i}{T_i} \right)_{\text{external}}$$

Obviously, the foregoing equation is not necessarily true. It is quite possible that there is an internal exchange of energy which does not involve any external element. Then

$$\Delta S = \sum_i \frac{q_i}{T_i} = \left(\sum_i \frac{q_i}{T_i} \right)_{\text{internal}} + \left(\sum_i \frac{q_i}{T_i} \right)_{\text{external}} \qquad (2\text{-}53)$$

Since the second law requires that

$$\left(\sum_i \frac{q_i}{T_i} \right)_{\text{internal}} \geq 0$$

Equation (2–53) becomes

$$\Delta S \geq \left(\sum_i \frac{q_i}{T_i} \right)_{\text{external}} \tag{2-54}$$

2. *The initial and final states of the system but nothing about the process that has taken place*

In this case, we may choose *any reversible process* which brings the system from the initial to the final state and calculate the increase in entropy as

$$\Delta S = \left(\sum_i \frac{q_i}{T_i} \right)_{\text{reversible process}} \tag{2-55}$$

The result is independent of the selection of the reversible process. To see this, suppose that there are two reversible processes which bring the system X from the initial state to the final state. If $(\Delta S)_A > (\Delta S)_B$, a contradiction to the second law can be shown as follows: Let the system X be operated from the initial to the final state through process A, and then from the final state to the initial state through process B. Consider the overall system which includes the system X and its surroundings Y. The system X is unchanged as it is brought back to the initial state. The only change in the over-all system is in Y. As a transfer of heat to the system X is the same as a transfer of heat away from Y, one has, for the total change of entropy:

$$\Delta S = -(\Delta S)_A + (\Delta S)_B < 0$$

which contradicts the second law, since the over-all system of X plus Y is obviously closed.

A similar contradiction can be shown if $(\Delta S)_A < (\Delta S)_B$. Therefore, Eq. (2–55) is independent of the process selected.

Example 2–6: Referring to Fig. 2–1, the piston and walls are assumed to be thermally insulated, and there is 0.1 kg of helium in the cylinder at a temperature of 25°C. By moving the piston upwards, the helium gas is expanded from an initial volume of 0.02 m³ to a final volume of 0.05 m³. Determine the final temperature and change of entropy of the gas under the following two circumstances:

(a) The piston moves slowly and the difference between F and pA is negligibly small.
(b) The piston moves suddenly and a vacuum is temporarily created in its wake.

The ratio C_p/C_V for helium is 5/3.

SOLUTION: For case (a), since the gas is always in equilibrium, there is no internal exchange of energy. Furthermore, as the piston and walls are thermally insulated, there is no exchange of heat between the gas and external objects. Therefore,

$$\Delta S = 0$$

As the expansion is adiabatic, Eq. (2–13) gives

$$T_2 = T_1\left(\frac{V_1}{V_2}\right)^{\gamma-1} = 298.1\left(\frac{0.02}{0.05}\right)^{2/3}$$

$$= 298.1° \times 0.543 = 162°K = -111°C$$

For case (b), since there is no work done on the piston by the gas and there is no heat exchange with outside, the internal energy of the gas remains unchanged. Consequently, the temperature remains unchanged.

As the kinetic energy of the gas molecules during the initial rush is converted into heat, there is an increase in entropy. The increase ΔS can be calculated by Eq. (2–55), using the reversible process of isothermal expansion. Since $dU = 0$, $dQ = p\,dV$, and

$$\Delta S = \int \frac{dQ}{T} = \int_{V_1}^{V_2} \frac{p\,dV}{T} = mR\int_{V_1}^{V_2} \frac{dV}{V}$$

$$= mR \ln \frac{V_2}{V_1} = \frac{0.1}{4} \times 8310 \times \ln \frac{0.05}{0.02}$$

$$= 191 \text{ joules/}°K$$

Example 2–7: An air-conditioner has the following data under steady state operation:

Outdoor temperature: 40°C

Indoor temperature: 20°C

Cooling capacity = 270,000 joules/minute

Input power: 1000 watts

Determine the total change in entropy per minute.

SOLUTION: Since there is no change in the air-conditioner itself, its entropy remains unchanged. The heat dissipated outdoors is

270,000 joules + 60,000 joules = 330,000 joules

$$\Delta S = \frac{330,000}{273.1 + 40} - \frac{270,000}{273.1 + 20} = 1053 - 920 = 133 \text{ joules/}°K$$

2-9. PROOF OF THE CONVERSE

Proof of Statement 2(a) from the second law is easily done by showing a contradiction. If a positive quantity of heat Q is transferred from a body at lower temperature T_2 to a body of higher temperature T_1, the change in entropy is

$$\Delta S = \frac{Q}{T_1} - \frac{Q}{T_2} < 0$$

This is in contradiction to the second law.

2-10. EXTENSION TO THERMOELECTRIC ENGINES

One point of paramount interest to electrical engineers is whether the second law applies to engines which generate electric energy or work from thermal energy or vice versa?

To answer the point, we note that, at least theoretically, lossless conversion between electrical and mechanical energies is possible. The free exchange between electrical and mechanical energies is *implicitly assumed* in the definition of electrical potential. It can also be verified from the $F = Bli$ and $e = Blv$ equations. Canceling Bl from these equations gives $Fv = ei$, which equates electrical power to mechanical power. We know also from experience that the limit of efficiency of an electric generator or motor is 100%, which is sometimes approached quite closely. An electric generator is not only basically reversible, but actually approaches being reversible in the limit of very large sizes.

As the generated or consumed electrical energy can be converted theoretically to, or from, an equal amount of mechanical energy, the second law must apply to both or neither. Therefore it applies to thermoelectric engines. Stated another way, electrical energy also has zero entropy.

Thus we see there are two kinds of energies in nature. The thermal energy Q at temperature T is chained by an entropy Q/T and kept from doing work freely. Electrical and mechanical energies are free to do work or convert into each other or can themselves become chained by dissipating into thermal energy. But the latter change is not reversible. These points confirm the classification of energy into orderly and disorderly types as discussed in Sec. 2–3.

2-11. ANALYSIS OF BASICALLY REVERSIBLE MACHINES

In its strict definition, a reversible machine operating in reverse completely reverses the energy conversion processes. No actual machine

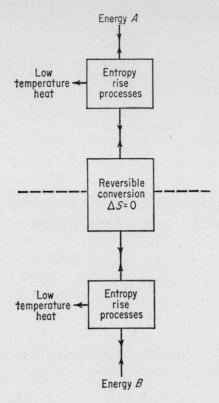

Fig. 2–8. Block Diagram Representation of a Basically Reversible Machine.

meets this description. For instance, an electric generator can be operated as an electric motor, but the generator losses which are converted into heat do not become motor gains and cause the machine to absorb heat from its surroundings.

A large number of machines are basically reversible, however, and can be represented by the energy conversion diagram of Fig. 2–8. The machine operation is separated into a reversible conversion process and an irreversible entropy rise process in each energy stage. The most common among the latter processes are listed below:

Table 2–1: Entropy Rise Processes

Electrical	i^2R loss, iron loss
Mechanical	Friction and windage loss
Thermal	Direct heat transfer from a hot substance to a cold substance

The advantage of separating out the entropy-rise processes is that the corollary of the second law can now be applied to the reversible conversion block. We have an equality sign to work with rather than an inequality sign, and quantitative results are obtained for this block. The entropy-rise processes are then calculated and used to modify the two sides of the reversible block.

In the special case of electromechanical energy conversion, the requirement of $\Delta S = 0$ means that the totality of mechanical energy is converted into electrical energy and vice versa. Any loss into thermal energy would cause an entropy rise and is not possible in the reversible block.

PART B.   FROM DUALITY OF MATTER TO SEMICONDUCTOR THEORY

An important phase of the recent progress in energy conversion is the development of new methods and new materials with suitable properties. Actually, the methods are not new, but with the old materials they were too inefficient to be of any practical value.

The development of new materials in this area was by no means a result of organized research and hard and persistent work alone. It was inspired by scientific thinking of the highest order, and in fact could not have happened without the development of quantum mechanics in the 1920's and the subsequent development of solid state physics and especially semiconductor theory. The subsequent sections give a brief summary of the basic concepts and key steps pacing this development. The emphasis is on the underlying logic or physical reasoning. The treatment is not meant to be an all-inclusive summary of the scientific facts used in the energy-conversion area, but to provide a framework upon which most of the relevant scientific facts can be attached.

2-12. THE DUALITY OF MATTER

From our daily experience, we have acquired distinctive notions of what is a particle, and what is a wave. The characteristic attribute of a particle is its *discreteness*. A particle has definite mass, momentum, and energy. The characteristic attribute of a wave motion is its possession of a *phase angle*. Several wave motions energized by coherent sources add vectorially at each point in space and produce what is known as a *diffraction pattern*. The two attributes are not mutually exclusive from a purely logical standpoint. Since our observation is limited to the *macroscopic* world (objects of ordinary sizes), in which an object is either a wave or a particle but not both, it is rather natural for us to assume that this distinction extends down to the *microscopic* world (objects of atomic size or smaller). Since the turn of the century, indirect and direct experimental evidence indicates that the extension of this distinction down to objects of atomic size is not in accord with physical reality.

In order to explain quantitatively the spectral distribution of black body radiation, Planck postulated that the energy of electromagnetic waves must be integer multiples of $h\nu$, where h is a universal constant which now bears his name and ν is the frequency of the electromagnetic wave. Planck's bold assumption was the first indication of the discrete nature of electromagnetic waves. A few years later, observing the existence of a threshold wavelength in photoelectric effect, Einstein went one step further to postulate that an electromagnetic wave is actually made up of discrete photons of energy $h\nu$. A third piece of experimental evidence which firmly established the particle nature of electromagnetic radiation is the Compton effect. From the momentum and angle of the recoil electron, and the change of wavelength between the incident and scattered X-ray beams, Compton gave a convincing verification that the momentum of a photon is h/λ, where λ is the wavelength c/ν of the X-ray. To complete the picture, Davisson and Germer's experiment on the diffraction of an electron beam by a crystal clearly demonstrated the wave aspect of an electron. The conclusion drawn from these experiments is that a physical object of atomic size has attributes characteristic of both a particle and a wave motion. Its two-sided nature is exhibited by

$$E = h\nu \tag{2-56}$$

$$p = h/\lambda \tag{2-57}$$

where E and p are its energy and momentum respectively, ν and λ are its frequency and wavelength, and h is the Planck constant 6.625×10^{-34} joule-sec.

2-13. HEISENBERG'S UNCERTAINTY PRINCIPLE

Accepting the duality of matter, Heisenberg made an observation which is of profound influence for the later development of science as well as philosophical thinking. Newtonian mechanics is based on the assumption that at any instant of time, the position and momentum of a particle (or a system of particles) can be ascertained to any degree of accuracy as desired. This set of values at the initial instant constitutes the initial condition. Once the initial condition is established, the subsequent motion of the system is completely determined by the laws of mechanics.

Heisenberg pointed out the incompatibility of this assumption with the duality of matter:

(1) In order to observe the position of a particle, it is necessary to have at least one photon incident on the particle and be deflected by it. Since the photon has finite momentum, the momentum of the particle is disturbed or changed by the position determination. The change in momentum is not exactly known and is proportional to the momentum of the photon. In order to determine the position x more accurately, the wavelength of the photon must be shorter. As $p = h/\lambda$, however, the shorter the photon wavelength, the larger the uncertainty in the momentum of the particle. From this line of reasoning, Heisenberg showed that the minimum uncertainties Δx and Δp satisfy

$$\Delta x \, \Delta p \geq \frac{h}{4} \tag{2-58}$$

Equation (2–58) means that position and momentum cannot be exactly determined simultaneously. Following similar reasoning, it was also shown

$$\Delta E \, \Delta t \geq \frac{h}{4} \tag{2-59}$$

where E is the energy of a photon and t is the time of its emission.

(2) As the uncertainties cited are not owing to any defect of the experiments, but to the basic duality of matter, they cast doubt on the very existence of an initial condition of exactly defined position and momentum, and with it on the entire Newtonian theory.

Besides casting doubt on the very foundation of Newtonian mechanics, the uncertainty principle also serves a constructive purpose: The motion of a particle or a system must be described probablistically rather than deterministically. Instead of using $\mathbf{x}(t)$,* which gives the exact position at each instant of time, a probability density function $\rho(\mathbf{x}, t)$ is used; $\rho(\mathbf{x}, t)$ is defined to mean that the probability of finding the particle in a volume element $d\tau$ about $\mathbf{x}$ is $\rho(\mathbf{x}, t) \, d\tau$. In this paragraph, as well as throughout the book, bold-faced letters are used to represent vectors. Thus, $\mathbf{x}$ represents the position vector (x, y, z).

---

* Bold face symbols represent vectors.

The use of $\rho(\mathbf{x}, t)$ to describe the motion of a particle can be readily modified to describe its wave nature also. As $\rho(\mathbf{x}, t)$ cannot be negative, it reminds one of the energy density function which is proportional to the square of the wave amplitude. The analogy suggests a complex wave function $\psi(\mathbf{x}, t)$ which is related to $\rho(\mathbf{x}, t)$ by

$$\rho(\mathbf{x}, t) = |\psi(\mathbf{x}, t)|^2 \tag{2–60}$$

As $\psi(\mathbf{x}, t)$ has both an amplitude and a phase (its angle in the complex plane), it presents a way of representing both the particle and wave aspects of matter in a simple coherent mathematical scheme.

2-14. SCHROEDINGER'S WAVE EQUATION

Mathematically speaking, classical mechanics is no more than a systematic method of finding the differential equation for $\mathbf{x}(t)$ and then its solution. Similarly, quantum mechanics is no more than a systematic method for finding the partial differential equation for $\psi(\mathbf{x}, t)$ and then its solution. Schroedinger solved the first part of the problem as follows: Consider a plane wave in the x direction with frequency ν and wavelength λ. Its wave function is

$$\psi = \psi_0 e^{i(kx - \omega t)} \tag{2–61}$$

where $k = 2\pi/\lambda$, $\omega = 2\pi\nu$, i is $\sqrt{-1}$, and ψ_0 is a constant. From Eq. (2–61),

$$\frac{\partial}{\partial x}\psi = ik\psi = \frac{2\pi i}{h}\frac{h}{\lambda}\psi = \frac{2\pi i}{h}p\psi \tag{2–62}$$

Equation (2–62) suggests that we can write the momentum variable p as a differential operator

$$p = -\frac{ih}{2\pi} \cdot \frac{\partial}{\partial x} \tag{2–63}$$

Similarly the energy E can be written as

$$E = \frac{ih}{2\pi} \cdot \frac{\partial}{\partial t} \tag{2–64}$$

Although Equation (2–63) and Eq. (2–64) are derived from a plane wave function, they are in such general forms that their application may not be limited to plane wave functions. Schroedinger made his brilliant contribution by applying these equations to the general case. In Newtonian mechanics, the total energy E can be written as

$$E = V(x, t) + \frac{1}{2m}p^2 \tag{2-65}$$

where $V(x, t)$ is the potential energy and $p^2/2m$ is the kinetic energy. In operator form, Eq. (2–65) becomes

$$\frac{ih}{2\pi} \cdot \frac{\partial}{\partial t} = V(x, t) + \frac{1}{2m}\left(-\frac{ih}{2\pi} \cdot \frac{\partial}{\partial x}\right)^2$$

Schroedinger's wave equation is obtained by letting the foregoing operator equation operate on ψ:

$$\frac{ih}{2\pi} \cdot \frac{\partial \psi}{\partial t} = V(x, t)\psi - \frac{h^2}{8\pi^2 m} \cdot \frac{\partial^2 \psi}{\partial x^2} \tag{2-66}$$

For the three-dimensional case, it is easy to show that Eq. (2–63) is replaced by

$$p_x = -\frac{ih}{2\pi} \cdot \frac{\partial}{\partial x}$$

$$p_y = -\frac{ih}{2\pi} \cdot \frac{\partial}{\partial y} \tag{2-67}$$

$$p_z = -\frac{ih}{2\pi} \cdot \frac{\partial}{\partial z}$$

and Eq. (2–66) is replaced by

$$\frac{ih}{2\pi} \cdot \frac{\partial \psi}{\partial t} = V(\mathbf{x}, t) - \frac{h^2}{8\pi^2 m^2}\left(\frac{\partial^2 \psi}{\partial x^2} + \frac{\partial^2 \psi}{\partial y^2} + \frac{\partial^2 \psi}{\partial z^2}\right) \tag{2-68}$$

Equations (2–66) and (2–68) are known as *Schroedinger's wave equations*. In addition to Eq. (2–68), ψ is required to satisfy two other conditions:

(a) Since the second partial derivatives must exist so that Eq. (2–68) can be meaningful, the first partial derivatives of ψ must exist and be continuous in x, y, and z.

(b) By its definition of being the probability density function, $\rho(\mathbf{x}, t)$ must satisfy

$$\int_\Omega \rho(\mathbf{x}, t) \, d\tau = 1$$

where Ω represents the entire accessible space. From Eq. (2–60), the foregoing can be rewritten as

$$\int_\Omega |\psi(\mathbf{x}, t)|^2 \, d\tau = 1 \tag{2-69}$$

These two conditions, together with Eq. (2-68), determine ψ completely.

Once ψ is solved in terms of x, y, z, and t, the probability density function $\rho(x, t)$ can be calculated from Eq. (2-60).

The place of Schroedinger's wave equation in quantum mechanics is approximately equivalent to that of Newton's second law in classical mechanics. Because of our unfamilarity with atomic phenomena, however, the greatest value of Schroedinger's equation is less in giving a solution to a relatively simple dynamical problem than in indicating a nature of the solution for more complex systems, as we shall see presently.

2-15. DISCRETE ENERGY STATES

Schroedinger's equation has a result of far-reaching consequence: the existence of allowed states with selected values of energy. In classical mechanics, a particle in a potential field $V(\mathbf{x})$ may have energy of any value, but this is no longer true in quantum mechanics.

In a potential field $V(\mathbf{x})$, the total energy E of a particle is a constant. Solving the operator equation (2-64) operating on ψ, we obtain

$$\psi(\mathbf{x}, t) = u(\mathbf{x})e^{-2\pi iEt/h} \tag{2-70}$$

where $u(\mathbf{x})$ is a complex-valued function of $\mathbf{x}$. Substitution of Eq. (2-70) into Eq. (2-68) and Eq. (2-69) gives

$$Eu = V(\mathbf{x})u - \frac{h^2}{8\pi^2 m}\left(\frac{\partial^2 u}{\partial x^2} + \frac{\partial^2 u}{\partial y^2} + \frac{\partial^2 u}{\partial z^2}\right) \tag{2-71}$$

$$\int |u(\mathbf{x})|^2 \, d\tau = 1 \tag{2-72}$$

In general, a solution $u(\mathbf{x})$ exists only for specific values of E. These values are called *eigenvalues* and the corresponding solutions $u(\mathbf{x})$ are called *eigenfunctions*. An example is given to illustrate this point.

Example 2-8: In a one-dimensional problem, the potential $V(x)$ is given as

$$V(x) = 0 \qquad |x| \leq a$$

$$V(x) = V_1 \qquad |x| > a$$

Determine the values of E for which non-trivial solutions of Schroedinger's wave equation exist.

SOLUTION: There are three ranges of values of E: (a) $0 < E < V_1$ (b) $E \geq V_1$, and (c) $E \leq 0$. We shall study these three cases in turn.

(a) $0 < E < V_1$
   Equation (2-71) can be written as

$$\frac{d^2u}{dx^2} + \frac{8\pi^2 m^2}{h^2}[E - V(x)]u = 0 \tag{2-73}$$

For $|x| \leq a$, the solution is

$$u = C_1 e^{ikx} + C_2 e^{-ikx}$$

For $x < -a$,

$$u = C_3 e^{\alpha x} + C_4 e^{-\alpha x} \tag{2-74}$$

and for $x > a$,

$$u = C_5 e^{\alpha x} + C_6 e^{-\alpha x}$$

where α and k are real positive constants given by the following equation

$$\alpha = \frac{2\pi}{h}\sqrt{2m(V_1 - E)}$$

$$k = \frac{2\pi}{h}\sqrt{2mE} \tag{2-75}$$

and $C_1, C_2, \ldots, C_6$ are constants to be determined. With only one dimension x, Eq. (2-72) becomes

$$\int_{-\infty}^{\infty} |u(x)|^2 \, dx = 1 \tag{2-76}$$

To satisfy Eq. (2-76), the integrand on the left-hand side of Eq. (2-76) must not diverge at $\pm \infty$. It follows that

$$C_4 = C_5 = 0$$

In order that u and du/dx be continuous at $x = \pm a$, we have

$$e^{-ika}C_1 + e^{ika}C_2 - e^{-\alpha a}C_3 = 0$$

$$ike^{-ika}C_1 - ike^{ika}C_2 - \alpha e^{-\alpha a}C_3 = 0$$

$$e^{ika}C_1 + e^{-ika}C_2 - e^{-\alpha a}C_6 = 0 \tag{2-77}$$

$$ike^{ika}C_1 - ike^{-ika}C_2 + \alpha e^{-\alpha a}C_6 = 0$$

The foregoing simultaneous equations can be satisfied by non-vanishing values of C_1, C_2, C_3, and C_6 only if the characteristic determinant vanishes:

$$\begin{vmatrix} e^{-ika} & e^{ika} & -e^{-\alpha a} & 0 \\ ike^{-ika} & -ike^{ika} & -\alpha e^{-\alpha a} & 0 \\ e^{ika} & e^{-ika} & 0 & -e^{-\alpha a} \\ ike^{ika} & -ike^{-ika} & 0 & \alpha e^{-\alpha a} \end{vmatrix} = 0$$

Multiplying the first row by $-\alpha$ and third row by α and adding the resulting rows to the second and fourth rows respectively give

$$\begin{vmatrix} e^{-ika} & e^{ika} & -e^{-\alpha a} & 0 \\ (ik - \alpha)e^{-ika} & (-ik - \alpha)e^{ika} & 0 & 0 \\ e^{ika} & e^{-ika} & 0 & -e^{-\alpha a} \\ (ik + \alpha)e^{ika} & (-ik + \alpha)e^{-ika} & 0 & 0 \end{vmatrix} = 0$$

Expanding the preceding expression gives

$$(ik + \alpha)^2 e^{2ika} - (\alpha - ik)^2 e^{-2ika} = 0 \tag{2-78}$$

Equation (2–78) can be written as

$$\frac{\alpha + ik}{\alpha - ik} = \pm e^{-2ika} \tag{2-79}$$

Equating the angle on the two sides of Eq. (2–79) gives

$$\tan^{-1}\frac{k}{\alpha} = \frac{n\pi}{2} - ka \tag{2-80}$$

where n is an integer. Equation (2–75) can be written in a more convenient form. Let an angle θ be defined by

$$E = V_1 \sin^2 \theta, \qquad 0 < \theta < \frac{\pi}{2} \tag{2-81}$$

Equations (2–75) can be written as

$$ka = z \sin \theta$$
$$\alpha a = z \cos \theta$$

where

$$z = \frac{2\pi a}{h}\sqrt{2mV_1}.$$

Equation (2–80) becomes

$$\theta = \frac{n\pi}{2} - z \sin \theta \tag{2–82}$$

Let N be the smallest integer satisfying $N\pi/2 \geq z$. There is a unique solution of θ for each value of $n = 1, 2, \ldots, N$. Correspondingly, Eq. (2–81) gives N values of E.

(b) $E \geq V_1$

There is no solution, as the integral of Eq. (2–72) is infinite unless $u = 0$.

(c) $E \leq 0$

The solution for $|x| \leq a$ becomes

$$u(x) = C_1 e^{\beta x} + C_2 e^{-\beta x}$$

where β is a real number. The reader can verify readily that the characteristic determinant never vanishes. Consequently there is no nontrivial solution.

In classical mechanics, the kinetic energy is never negative. As $V(x)$ is non-negative for the present problem, the total energy E cannot be negative. This conclusion checks with case (c). On the other hand, if the total energy of the particle is greater than V_1, it would certainly escape from the potential well. There cannot be a steady state solution which gives the particle a finite probability of staying inside the potential well. Thus, the conclusions of classical mechanics and quantum mechanics are the same also for case (b). The main difference is in case (a). In classical mechanics, the energy E of a particle staying inside the potential well can be anywhere from 0 to V_1. In quantum mechanics, only a few values of E are possible. These are the eigenvalues of E as obtained in Ex. 2–8. Although we have cited only a specific example here, this vital difference is nevertheless general enough. In the theory of differential equations, it is well established that non-trivial solutions of Eq. (2–71) and Eq. (2–72) exist only for eigenvalues of E.

For each eigenvalue of E, there is a solution $u(\mathbf{x})$. These solutions are called *eigenfunctions*. The possible existence of a particle so described is called an *allowed state*, or simply a *state* of the system.

2-16. SYSTEMS WITH MANY PARTICLES, BOSONS AND FERMIONS

For a system with many closely coupled particles, it is indeed difficult to find a mathematical solution. There is a definite value of energy for the entire system, but the energy of any one particle becomes meaningless. Fortunately, except for the notable example of interactions between nucleons inside a nucleus, the coupling between particles is usually sufficiently loose for the following approximation to hold:

Each particle can be regarded as moving alone in a fixed potential field $V(\mathbf{x})$, and only the average total effect of the other particles is taken into consideration as a modification of $V(\mathbf{x})$. Outstanding examples of this type of approximation are

1. *Hartree's approximate model of an atom*

In solving for the wave function of each electron, the effects of the other electrons and the nucleus are lumped together and represented by a central field $V(\mathbf{x}) = V(r)$ where r is the scalar distance from the nucleus.

2. *Model for a crystal*

The atomic nuclei and interior orbital electrons are represented as a periodic potential of three dimensions in which the valence electrons move. In writing the wave equation for each electron, the other electrons are considered uniformly distributed throughout the lattice structure. Thus, the potential $V(\mathbf{x})$ is that produced by a positively charged lattice immersed in a negatively charged background. The over-all charge density is zero.

As the wave equation for each electron is the same, the eigenvalues of E and allowed states for each electron are also the same. The state of the entire system of particles is specified by the number of particles in each state.

Both theoretical considerations and experimental evidence show that there are two types of particles in nature: *Bosons* and *Fermions*. There can be any number of Bosons in the same state, but there can be no more than one Fermion to each state. Among the well-known elementary particles, only the photons are Bosons. Electrons, protons, and neutrons are all Fermions.

2-17. DISTRIBUTION OF PARTICLES IN THE ALLOWED STATES

From rather general considerations, Maxwell and Boltzmann derived a very useful law of distribution. Consider a subsystem which may be in any one of several states n, $n = 1, 2 \ldots$. Its energy in state n is E_n, and it is in constant contact with an infinitely larger system at temperature T. The probability that the subsystem has energy E_n was shown to be

$$p(n) = Ke^{-E_n/kT} \qquad (2\text{-}83)$$

where $k = 1.3804 \times 10^{-23}$ joule/deg, and is known as the *Boltzmann constant* and K is a proportionality constant.

The constant K can be easily evaluated. Since the subsystem must be in one or the other of the states

$$\sum_n p(n) = \sum_n K e^{-E_n/kT} = 1 \qquad (2\text{-}84)$$

The constant K is evaluated from Eq. (2–84) and the result is then substituted into Eq. (2–83) to give

$$p(n) = \frac{e^{-E_n/kT}}{\sum e^{-E_n/kT}} \qquad (2\text{-}85)$$

Using the foregoing formula, an expression for the average number of particles in each state will now be derived. Let the eigenvalue of energy of the ith state be denoted E_i. We note that if an arbitrary constant C is added to $V(\mathbf{x})$ of Eq. (2–71), the physical problem is not changed but all the E_i's, $i = 1, 2, 3$, are increased by C. Thus only the relative values of the E_i's are meaningful. Let the ith state itself be considered a subsystem. The condition or the "state" of the subsystem is then the number of particles in it. The energy per particle is $E_i - E_0$, where E_0 is some reference level of energy and is the same for all values of i. The energy of the subsystem with n particles in it is

$$E_n = n(E_i - E_0) \qquad (2\text{-}86)$$

Substituting Eq. (2–86) into Eq. (2–85) gives the probability of having n particles in state i

$$p(n) = \frac{e^{-n(E_i - E_0)/kT}}{\sum e^{-n(E_i - E_0)/kT}} \qquad (2\text{-}87)$$

The average number of particles in state i is

$$\overline{n_i} = \sum_n n p(n) = \frac{\displaystyle\sum_n n e^{-n(E_i - E_0)/kT}}{\displaystyle\sum_n e^{-n(E_i - E_0)/kT}} \qquad (2\text{-}88)$$

For Fermions, $n = 0, 1$, and Eq. (2–88) gives

$$\overline{n_i} = \frac{e^{-(E_i - E_0)/kT}}{1 + e^{-(E_i - E_0)/kT}}$$

$$= \frac{1}{e^{(E_i - E_0)/kT} + 1}$$

The number $\overline{n}_i$ is always less than unity and is known as the *Fermi factor* $f(E_i)$:

$$f(E_i) \equiv \overline{n}_i = \frac{1}{e^{(E_i - E_0)/kT} + 1} \qquad (2\text{–}89)$$

The reference energy level E_0 is called the *Fermi level*. Its value is determined by the condition that the total number of particles is a fixed or known number N:

$$\sum_i f(E_i) = \sum_i \frac{1}{e^{(E_i - E_0)/kT} + 1} = N \qquad (2\text{–}90)$$

where the summation is taken over all the states i of the system.

On the surface, the reasoning for Eq. (2–90) may appear to be no more than "fudging" for the right answer. There is, however, a very plausible explanation. The only type of particles for which Eq. (2–89) has extensive application are the electrons. If E_0 is initially too high and there are too many electrons, the potential energy $V(\mathbf{x})$ of Eq. (2–71) is raised owing to the electrostatic interaction and consequently all the E_i's are raised relative to the reference level E_0. The same mathematical relation would result if we lower E_0 instead of changing the E_i's. With increased $E_i - E_0$, the total number of electrons N as calculated from Eq. (2–89) is reduced, and the process arrives at a natural balance between E_0 and N.

Equation (2–89) shows that there is a natural tendency for Fermions to stay at low energy. At absolute zero temperature, only the states with lowest energy are occupied. The demarcation line between occupied and unoccupied states becomes blurred as the temperature is increased and more and more states of higher energy are occupied.

A plot of the Fermi factor is given in Fig. 2–9. It is noted that at room temperature (300°K) $f(E) \cong 1$ for $E < E_0 - 0.1$ ev and $f(E) \cong 0$ for $E > E_0 + 0.1$ ev.

For Bosons, $n = 0, 1, 2 \ldots$ and is unlimited in its possible values. Let λ denote $e^{-(E_i - E_0)/kT}$. Equation (2–88) can be written as

$$\overline{n}_i = \frac{\sum\limits_n n\lambda^n}{\sum\limits_n \lambda^n} \qquad (2\text{–}91)$$

We assume that the relative energy of each particle is always positive

$$E_i - E_0 > 0 \qquad (2\text{–}92)$$

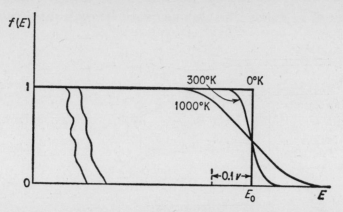

Fig. 2-9. FERMI FACTOR $f(E)$ VERSUS E.

Inequality (2-92) will be justified later. From expression (2-92) it follows that $\lambda < 1$ and

$$\sum_{n=0}^{n=\infty} \lambda^n = \frac{1}{1 - \lambda}$$

$$\sum_{n=0}^{n=\infty} n\lambda^n = \frac{\lambda}{(1 - \lambda)^2}$$

Substituting the above expressions into Eq. (2-91) gives

$$\overline{n_i} = \frac{\lambda/(1 - \lambda)^2}{1/(1 - \lambda)} = \frac{\lambda}{1 - \lambda} = \frac{1}{e^{(E_i - E_0)/kT} - 1} \tag{2-93}$$

Equations (2-89) and (2-93) are very similar to each other except for the sign on the denominator.

Equation (2-93) has so far been applied only to systems with $E_i - E_0 = h\nu$ where ν is either the frequency of the photon or the frequency of the harmonic oscillator. Thus expression (2-92) is valid in both cases.

2-18. THE ALLOWED STATES FOR SOLIDS, ENERGY BANDS

The mathematical model for an atom is that of a number of electrons moving in a potential well $V(\mathbf{x})$. The atomic nucleus does not enter into the problem except that it gives rise to the potential well $V(\mathbf{x})$. Similar to Ex. 2-8, the allowed energy levels are discrete, as shown in Fig. 2-10(a).

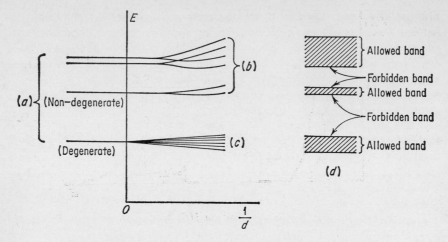

Fig. 2-10. Split of Energy Levels When Atoms are Brought Together: (a) Discrete Energy Levels of a Single Atom; (b) Energy Levels versus $1/d$, where d is the Distance between Two Atoms; (c) Originally Degenerate Energy Levels versus $1/d$; (d) Energy Bands of Solids.

When we bring two atoms closer and closer together, there is a greater and greater probability that the electrons in one atom may travel to the other atom and vice versa. It becomes meaningless to speak of the energy levels of one atom or the other; one must speak of the energy levels of the two atoms together. The situation is quite similar to that of coupling two resonant circuits of the same frequency. The resonant frequency is split into two for the coupled circuits as a whole, and the separation between the resonant frequencies is increased as the coupling becomes closer.

Figure 2-10(b) illustrates variations of allowed energy levels with the reciprocal of the distance as two identical atoms are brought together. When the two atoms are infinitely apart ($1/d = 0$), the energy levels are identical with that of a single atom. As the distance d becomes smaller and smaller, each level splits into two, and the separation between the pairs of levels becomes larger and larger. The levels which are originally close together are now intermixed.

What happens then when billions and billions of atoms are packed together as they are in any minute piece of solid large enough to be seen by the naked eye? The interatomic distances have definite values and do not change with the size of the material. As the interaction is between neighboring atoms, the energy of interaction per atom also has definite values. Consequently, the maximum separation between all the energy levels which are originated from the same energy level is fixed and does not increase with the size of the material. Thus billions and billions of energy levels are packed into a relatively small spacing. The situation is illustrated in Fig. 2–10(d). The allowed energy levels are crowded into a few bands with empty spaces between. The former are called *allowed bands* and the latter are called *forbidden bands*.

The above gives a simple explanation of the energy-band structure in solids. A few details remain to be clarified.

1. *Degenerate states.* As discussed previously, each allowed state has a fixed value of energy. Sometimes two or more states with distinctly different wave functions have the same energy, or to put it in another way, there are n states on the same energy level. The latter is then called *n-fold degenerate.*

Usually degenerate energy levels become *non-degenerate* when an external disturbance is applied. Suppose a certain atomic energy level is threefold degenerate. When two such atoms are brought together, the energy level splits into six, as illustrated in Fig. 2–10(c).

2. *Shifts in energy levels.* It sometimes happens that atomic energy levels which are originally close together or are degenerate split into different allowed bands when a solid is formed. This is always the case with covalence bands. For instance, there are eight states in the partially occupied shell of a silicon atom. Four of the eight go into one band (*the valence band*) and the other four go into an adjacent band (*the conduction band*) when silicon crystal is formed.

3. Owing to the large number of allowed states in a solid, it is no longer possible to enumerate the energy levels. A feasible way of describing the energy levels is to give an expression for the number of states within a given energy range $E \pm \Delta E/2$. For sufficiently small ΔE, this number is proportional to ΔE and is a function of the mean energy E:

$$N_{\Delta E} = W(E)\ \Delta E \qquad (2\text{–}94)$$

The function $W(E)$ is the density of states or the number of states per unit range of energy. It is zero in a forbidden band.

2-19. CONDUCTION OF ELECTRICITY, ELECTRONS AND HOLES

If an allowed band is empty, there is no electron in it to conduct electricity. If an allowed band is full, the electrons in it do not take part in the conduction of electricity either. Only electrons in a partially filled band conduct electricity.

The explanation is as follows: A state has momentum associated with it as well as energy. From symmetry considerations, the momenta of the states are equally distributed in all directions. When an electric field is applied in the minus x direction, it creates a tendency for the electrons to transfer to states with higher momenta in the x direction. If the energy band is only partially filled, there are many unoccupied states with higher momenta in the x direction and only slightly higher energy on the average. The afore-mentioned tendency becomes realized, and the electrons have an average momentum in the x direction. If the energy band is completely filled, the only possibility open to the electrons is skipping a forbidden band and transferring to the next allowed band. Even with the strongest applied field, however, the perturbing energy is of the order of

electronic charge $\times$ field intensity $\times$ atomic dimension

$$= e \times 10^6 \text{ volts}/m \times 10^{-10}m = 10^{-4} \text{ ev}$$

As the width of a forbidden band is of the order of 1 ev or larger, a small perturbation of the order of 10^{-4} ev is quite incapable of causing any electron to skip a forbidden band. Thus, no change in electronic states can occur, and the average momentum of the electrons remains zero.

An important outgrowth of the concept that electrons which completely fill an energy band do not take part in conduction of electricity is the concept of "holes" as charge carriers. If an allowed band is nearly empty, the electrons behave like negatively charged particles in empty space. In other words, they conduct like electrons. If an allowed band is nearly full, the aggregated motion of the electrons gives exactly the same effects as conduction by positively charged carriers. The reason is as follows: With the states nearly filled up, most of the electrons have no opportunity to change to a state with higher momentum in the x direction (opposite to applied field) except the few electrons near the empty states (or holes) with momenta somewhat less than that of the empty states. These electrons do transfer and leave new empty states behind. Consequently we see the holes gaining higher and higher momentum in the $-x$ direction. As a completely filled energy band does not conduct electricity, it can be used as a reference for nothing happening. In this background of filled states, the holes are positively charged particles. Thus we see a picture of positively charged particles moving in the $-x$ direction.

Figure 2-11 gives an approximate illustration of the situation: Nine balls occupy ten spaces, and the rule of the game directs that the ball immediately to the left of the empty space move into it. The apparent picture is that of a hole moving from right to left. We may raise the objection that the hole not only moves jerkily but most of the time it is cut in two. But the objection is not meaningful in quantum mechanics. If the mo-

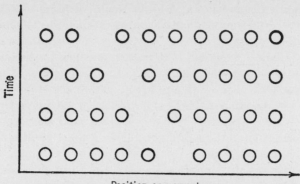

Position or momentum

Fig. 2-11. AN APPROXIMATE ILLUSTRATION OF THE MOTION OF HOLES.

mentum of an electron is known ever so approximately, its position cannot be completely known. Thus, all we can know about the hole is its approximate position and approximated momentum. Although the foregoing argument is not conclusive, it has been shown mathematically in quantum mechanics that a hole behaves exactly like a positively charged particle. It has mass, energy, momentum, and velocity and can be treated approximately as a positively charged particle in every way.

2-20. CONDUCTORS, INSULATORS, SEMICONDUCTORS, AND DOPING

Figure 2-12 illustrates the energy bands and the way these bands are filled at 0° absolute temperature for five different types of materials. The completely filled bands are called *valence bands* and the allowed bands which are empty or half-empty are called *conduction bands*. The conduction band of lowest energy and the valence band of highest energy are separated by a *forbidden band*. The width of the latter is called the *energy gap*. These three bands are most important in determining the properties of the solid. In the following, the terms *conduction band*, *valence band*, and *forbidden band* are meant for the conduction band *of lowest energy*, the valence band *of highest energy*, and the forbidden band in between.

In Fig. 2-12(a), the conduction band is partially filled, and consequently the material conducts electricity. Most metals have this structure.

In Fig. 2-12(b), the conduction band is completely empty and the valence band is completely full; consequently the material is a good insulator.

An intrinsic semiconductor has exactly the same band structure as an insulator. Its energy gap, however, is smaller, as illustrated in Fig. 2-12(c).

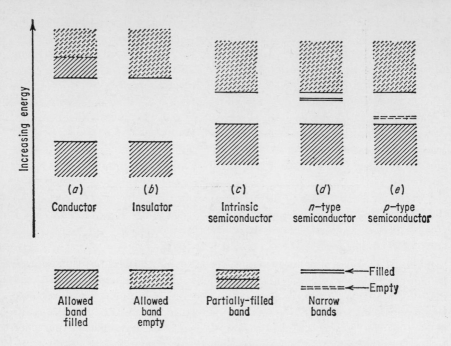

Fig. 2–12. ENERGY BANDS AND DISTRIBUTION OF ELECTRONS AT 0°K: (a) CONDUCTOR;   (b) INSULATOR;   (c) INTRINSIC SEMICONDUCTOR;   (d) n-TYPE SEMICONDUCTOR;   (e) p-TYPE SEMICONDUCTOR.

The energy gap of an insulator is several electron volts, whereas that of a semiconductor is about 1 electron volt or less.

The process of doping replaces a minute fraction of the atoms of the pure crystal with atoms of a different but similar type. If the latter atoms have a slightly higher positive nuclear charge, one or two more electrons are needed to neutralize each impurity atom in addition to the correct number for forming crystalline bonds. These electrons orbit loosely about the impurity atoms which are then called *donors*. The energy band structure is shown in Fig. 2–12(d). Note that a narrow filled band is introduced at a position slightly below the conduction band. The narrow filled band represents the energy levels of the extra electrons.

If the impurity atoms are of a type with slightly lower positive nuclear charge, their orbital electrons are less than the correct number for forming crystalline bonds. Consequently, some of the nearby states are empty and the holes so created orbit loosely about the impurity atoms. A part of the valence band is split out to form a narrow unfilled band right above it as illustrated in Fig. 2–12(e). In Fig. 2–12(d) and (e), we still refer to the original conduction and valence bands as conduction and valence bands, and the narrow bands generated by the impurities as *impurity bands*.

At $0°K$, the material represented by Fig. 2-12(a) is a conductor, but all the materials represented by Fig. 2-12(b), (c), (d), and (e) are insulators.

At room temperature, kT is approximately $\frac{1}{40}$ of an electron volt. Equation (2-89) shows that there is a diffusion of electrons from the lower energy levels to the higher levels. The redistributions of electrons are illustrated in Fig. 2-13. In Fig. 2-13(a), the dividing line between occupied and unoccupied states are blurred, but the material remains a good conductor. In Fig. 2-13(b), owing to the exponential factor of Eq. (2-89) and the wide energy gap, a very negligible number of electrons are raised from the valence band into the conduction band, and the material remains a good insulator. In Fig. 2-13(c) there are a very small but noticeable number of electrons raised from the valence band into the conduction band. Consequently, the number of holes in the valence band is equal to the number of electrons in the conduction band. The two types of carriers are equally responsible for making an intrinsic semiconductor a poor insulator. In Fig. 2-13(d), a substantial number of electrons from the impurity band move into the conduction band, and the material becomes a conductor with negatively charged carriers. In Fig. 2-13(e), a substantial number of electrons from the valence band move into the impurity band and the material becomes a conductor with positively charged carriers (holes).

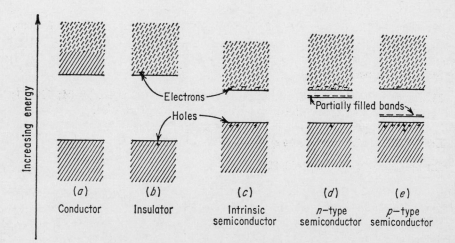

Fig. 2-13. ENERGY BANDS AND DISTRIBUTION OF ELECTRONS AT ROOM TEMPERATURE: (a) CONDUCTOR; (b) INSULATOR; (c) INTRINSIC SEMICONDUCTOR; (d) n-TYPE SEMICONDUCTOR; (e) p-TYPE SEMICONDUCTOR.

REFERENCES

First Law of Thermodynamics

1. Zemansky, M. W., *Heat and Thermodynamics*, 4th ed., pp. 56–76. New York: McGraw-Hill Book Co., 1957.

2. Lewis, G. N., M. Randall, K. S. Pitzer, and L. Brewer, *Thermodynamics*, 2nd ed., pp. 28–50. New York: McGraw-Hill Book Co., 1961.

3. Rossini, F. D., *Chemical Thermodynamics*, pp. 33–38; 52–58. New York: John Wiley & Sons, 1950.

4. Soo, S. L., *Analytical Thermodynamics*, pp. 48–65. Engelwood Cliffs, N. J.: Prentice-Hall, 1962.

Second Law of Thermodynamics, Entropy

5. Zemansky, M. W., [1, 139–94].

6. Lewis, G. N., *et al.*, [2, 75–98].

7. Rossini, F. D., [3, 67–91].

8. Soo, S. L., [4, 141–67].

Duality of Matter, Uncertainty Principle, Schroedinger's Equation

9. Schiff, L. I., *Quantum Mechanics*, pp. 1–25. New York: McGraw-Hill Book Co., 1949.

10. Sproull, R. L., *Modern Physics*, pp. 73–146. New York: John Wiley & Sons, 1956.

Maxwell-Boltzmann, Fermi-Dirac, Einstein-Bose Distributions

11. Landau, L. D., and E. M. Lifshitz, *Statistical Physics*, pp. 78–84; 110–13; 152–54. Reading, Mass.: Addison-Wesley Publishing Co., 1958.

Energy Bands of Solids, Theory of Conduction

12. Sproull, R. L., [10, 229–62, 325–39].

PROBLEMS

2–1. An air-conditioner operates at a room temperature of 70°F and outdoor temperature of 100°F. It draws 7.5 amp at 120 volts and 95% power factor, and has a cooling capacity of 8000 Btu per hour. How many Btu per hour is dissipated outdoors? (1 Btu = 2.93×10^{-4} kwh.)

2-2. An electric fan motor delivers 25 watts to the fan at an efficiency of 20%. How much heat in Btu is added to the room per hour? If by using a motor of better design, its efficiency is increased to 50% while the fan load remains unchanged, what is the new figure of heat added to the room per hour?

2-3. The temperature rise of a motor frame is approximately proportional to the rate at which heat is generated through all kinds of losses in the motor. For the inefficient fan motor of Prob. 2-2, the motor frame temperature is 160°F while the room temperature is 85°F. What is the motor frame temperature of the improved motor, assuming that the room temperature is unchanged?

2-4. If 1 kg of ice at 0°C and 2 kg of water at 85°C are brought together, what is the temperature of the resulting substance?

2-5. Calculate the total entropy rise in cal/°K for Prob. 2-4.

2-6. Calculate the total entropy rise per hour in Btu/°F for the two cases of Prob. 2-2 and Prob. 2-3. Assume that there is no further change in motor temperature.

2-7. Calculate the total entropy rise per hour in Btu/°F for Prob. 2-1.

2-8. In Prob. 2-1, an engineer is assigned to the job of trying to improve the performance of the air-conditioner. He started by measuring the temperatures T_e of the evaporating coil (cooling coil) and T_c of the condensing coil (heating coil) respectively. He might try to improve the motor compressor unit so that it will work better between the two coils; he might try to improve the affectiveness of the two coils; or he might do something else. Under the operating condition of Prob. 2-1, the measured temperatures are

(a) $T_e = 60°F$, $T_c = 115°F$

(b) $T_e = 30°F$, $T_c = 175°F$

(c) $T_e = 10°F$, $T_c = 200°F$

What should the engineer do in each case?

2-9. A steam turbine-generator has a boiler temperature of 540°F and a condensing steam temperature of 140°F. Heat is delivered to the boiler at the rate of 1,000,000 Btu per hour. Suppose only 50% of the Carnot efficiency is realized by the turbine-generator unit. What is the output power in kwh? What is the output power if the boiler temperature is raised to 940°F?

2-10. The indoor temperature is 70°F and the outdoor temperature is 20°F. Calculate the kwh required per day to give a heating effect of 20,000 Btu per hour for each of the following schemes:

(a) Direct electric heating
(b) Using a Carnot engine heat pump

2–11. In quantum mechanics, the expected value of a dynamic variable A is given as

$$\langle A \rangle = \int_\Omega \bar{\psi} A \psi \, d\tau \tag{P2–11–1}$$

where $\bar{\psi}$ is the complex conjugate of ψ. Note that, in case A is not an operator but an ordinary function of $\mathbf{x}$ and t, the preceding expression is reduced to the usual method of taking average:

$$\langle A \rangle = \int_\Omega A(\mathbf{x}, t) \rho(\mathbf{x}, t) \, d\tau$$

Show that for the wave function

$$u(x) = C e^{ikx} e^{-(x-x_0)^2/2a^2} \tag{P2–11–2}$$

the following expected values are obtained:

$$\langle x \rangle = x_0$$

$$\langle (x - x_0)^2 \rangle = \frac{a^2}{2}$$

$$\langle p_x \rangle = \frac{hk}{2\pi}$$

$$\langle (p_x - \langle p_x \rangle)^2 \rangle = \frac{h^2}{8\pi^2 a^2}$$

Let Δp_x and Δx denote the rms uncertainties

$$\Delta p_x \equiv \sqrt{\langle (p_x - \langle p_x \rangle)^2 \rangle}$$

$$\Delta x \equiv \sqrt{\langle (x - x_0)^2 \rangle}$$

Show that

$$\Delta p_x \, \Delta x = \frac{h}{4\pi}$$

Equation (P2–11–2) describes a "wave packet with minimum rms uncertainty." In general,

$$\Delta p \, \Delta q \geq \frac{h}{4\pi} \tag{P2–11–3}$$

The foregoing equation is a more precise statement of Heisenberg's uncertainty relation.

2–12. For the special case of V_1 approaching infinity in Ex. 2–8 find

(a) An expression for the energy eigenvalues E_n

(b) The eigenfunction $u(x)$ for each E_n

2-13. In Einstein's theory of specific heat for solids, the solid is regarded as a system of $3N$ independent oscillators with natural frequency ν. Show that for one mole of the substance, the internal energy U and specific heat $C(C_V = C_p = C$ for solids) are given as

$$U = \frac{3N_0 h\nu}{e^{h\nu/kT} - 1}$$

$$C = 3Rf(T/\beta)$$

where R is the universal gas constant, β is $h\nu/k$ and

$$f(x) = \frac{e^{1/x}}{x^2(e^{1/x} - 1)^2}$$

CHAPTER THREE

THERMOELECTRIC ENGINES

A primitive version of the thermoelectric engine, the thermal couple, has been known for many years. Until very recently, however, the principle was applied only to measurements. The difficulty was that the useful thermoelectric effects for most materials are at least an order of magnitude smaller compared to the wasteful effects of i^2R loss and conduction of heat. Research work on semiconducting materials in recent years has finally brought the two types of effects to the same order of magnitude. Presently, the thermoelectric engines are useful as energy converters in special applications and also as a heat pump for regulating the temperature of electronic components. With further improvements in material, the method is very likely to be commercially competitive with conventional ways of generating electricity.

This chapter describes the basic principles involved, design equations for these engines, pertinent properties of material, and the underlying electron theory which explains these effects. The electron theory will provide the reader with a deeper understanding of the physical nature of thermoelectric effects, but is not essential to apparatus design.

3-1. THERMOELECTRIC EFFECTS

Thermoelectricity functions in a way much similar to the distilling of water. If we put water in both ends of an inverted U pipe as shown in Fig. 3-1(a), heat one end, and cool the other, we shall soon find the water in the heated end evaporated and condensed in the cooled end. There is a transportation of water molecules from the hot end to the cold end. Similarly, when we

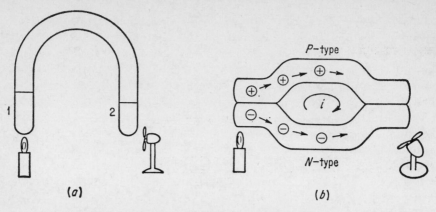

Fig. 3-1. The Physical Origin of Seebeck e.m.f.: (a) An Analogy; (b) Flows of Electrons and Holes in a Semiconductor Thermocouple.

heat one junction of a semiconductor thermocouple, the electrons are "evaporated" or raised from the valence band to the conduction band. For each electron "evaporated," there is a vacancy or hole left behind, and thus an electron travels to the cold junction via the n-type material, and the hole travels to the cold junction via the p-type material, as shown in Fig. 3-1(b). They reunite at the cold junction. Here the electrons drop back into the holes and release some energy to the cold junction. As the charges carried by the holes and electrons are opposed to each other, there is, in effect, a flow of positive current as indicated by i in Fig. 3-1(b).

The reader may ask why don't some of the electrons go from the hot junction to the cold junction through the p-type material, and some of the holes go to the same end through the n-type material? Because of the abundance of holes on the p side, almost all the electrons which get to the p side recombine with the holes immediately. The same thing happens to the holes which get into the n side. The net effect is that these holes and electrons may as well not have been separated at the hot junction at all.

Now let us return to Fig. 3-1(b). If the thermocouple is opened somewhere along the circuit, the tendency for the current i to flow develops into an emf. This is called the Seebeck emf, and the effect is called the *Seebeck effect.*

At the hot junction, or junction 1, both holes and electrons are moving away from the junction. To make up for the loss of these charge carriers, electrons are raised from the valence band to the conduction band to create new pairs of electrons and holes. As it takes energy to do this, heat is absorbed at junction 1. Similarly, as an electron drops into a hole at junction 2, it gives up its surplus energy. Thus heat is released at junction 2.

The number of valence electrons raised to the conduction band per second at junction 1, and the number of conduction electrons dropped back to the valence band per second at junction 2 are proportional to i. Thus the rate of heat absorbed at junction 1 and the rate of heat released at junction 2 are proportional to i. Furthermore, that junction 1 is hotter than junction 2 is purely incidental. If junction 1 is colder than junction 2, but i is maintained in the same direction by introducing a battery into the circuit, electrons are still raised from valence band to conduction band at junction 1 and dropped back to valence band at junction 2. Heat is still absorbed at junction 1 and released at junction 2. The absorption or release of heat when an electric current is sent through a junction is called the *Peltier effect.*

A third and more subtle effect exists because of the temperature gradient along each conductor. The charge carriers (electrons or holes) at one temperature have very different average energy from the same charge carriers in the same conductor but at a different temperature. This average energy is maintained through frequent collisions with the crystal lattice. If the average energy of the arriving charge carriers is lower, they absorb energy along the path through collisions with the crystal lattice, which in turn absorbs heat from the surroundings. The flow of energy is reversed if the average energy of the arriving charge carriers is higher.

The absorption or release of heat when an electric current passes through a conductor with a temperature gradient is called the *Thomson effect.*

The three effects just discussed, the Seebeck effect, the Peltier effect, and the Thomson effect are given the generic name, *thermoelectric effects.* Their existence is not limited to semiconductors, as they exist with metals and junctions of different metals as well. In metals, however, these effects are relatively small and the reason for their existence is more obscure and subtle.

The previous discussion is aimed at acquainting the reader with the physical natures of these effects. For engineering purposes, we shall apply the two laws of thermodynamics to these effects to derive some precise relationships which are then used to formulate a procedure for analysis and design of the various types of thermoelectric energy converters. In order that the derivations be perfectly general, we shall forego the semiconductor theory and define the thermoelectric effects in terms of external measurements only.

The Seebeck Effect. Referring to Fig. 3–2(a), two dissimilar conducting or semiconducting materials A and B are joined at both ends. If there is a temperature difference between the two terminals, $T_1 \neq T_2$, an emf e_{ab} will appear between B_1 and B_2. This effect is called the *Seebeck effect.*

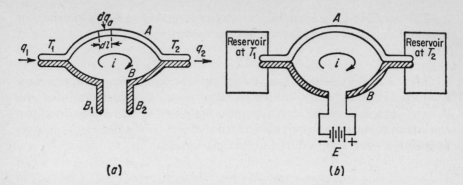

Fig. 3–2. THE BASIC THERMOELECTRIC ENGINE–A THERMO-
COUPLE: (**a**) MATHEMATICAL QUANTITIES DEFINING THE
THERMOELECTRIC EFFECTS; (**b**) A BASIC THERMOELECTRIC
GENERATOR.

To measure e_{ab}, we must make certain that the temperature is the same
at B_1 and B_2. Otherwise, thermoelectric effects between B and the third
metal which connects B_1 and B_2 to the meter element will modify the results
appreciably.

The Seebeck emf e_{ab} is defined positive if the current tends to flow from
A to B at the cold junction.

The Peltier Effect. Now let us connect B_1 to B_2 directly or through a
battery. A current i flows around the closed circuit. It is found that heat
is either absorbed or generated at the junctions. Let us say heat q_1 is absorbed at junction 1. If there is a heat reservoir which maintains junction
1 at temperature T_1, heat will flow from the reservoir into the junction as
indicated by the arrow in Fig. 3–2(a). If there is no such reservoir, junction
1 must absorb heat from itself, that means that it will cool down to a lower
temperature.

The rate of flow of heat q_1 is proportional to i:

$$q_1(T) = \pi_{ab}(T)i \tag{3-1}$$

The sign convention of Eq. (3–1) implies the following:

1. If we reverse the direction of i, q_1 becomes negative, and heat
   $|q_1|$ is generated at the junction.
2. A positive $\pi_{ab}(T)$ means that heat is absorbed at the junction if a
   positive current flows from B to A, and is generated at the junction
   if a positive current flows from A to B.

The coefficient π_{ab} is called the *Peltier coefficient* and is a function of temperature. From the definition of π_{ab} it follows that

$$\pi_{ab}(T) = -\pi_{ba}(T) \qquad (3\text{-}2)$$

The Thomson Effect. In the presence of a temperature gradient along a conducting material, heat is absorbed or released in proportion to the current passing through it. This effect is called the *Thomson effect*. The rate at which heat is absorbed in a small segment of conductor dl is proportional to the current i and the temperature gradient

$$dq = \tau(T)i\,\frac{dT}{dl}\,dl \qquad (3\text{-}3)$$

In Eq. (3-3), positive i means that a positive current is flowing in the direction of increasing l. A positive dq means that heat is absorbed from the surroundings. The significances of the signs of dq and $\tau(T)$ are similar to that of q_1 and $\pi(T)$ which have already been explained for the Peltier effect.

The Thomson coefficient $\tau(T)$ can be positive or negative, depending on the material.

Before proceeding further, the beginner must grasp one crucial point about the thermoelectric effects. Normally, if we transfer heat to a material, it gets hot. If we transfer the required Peltier heat and Thomson heat to the elements A and B with the passage of current, however, the temperatures of these elements are not changed. A simple concept to use is that *the Peltier and Thomson effects represent the heat carried away with the passage of current* at the junction and inside the elements respectively.

3-2. REVERSIBLE EFFECTS OF THE THERMOELECTRIC ENGINE: KELVIN'S RELATIONS

Figure 3-2(b) shows an elementary form of a thermoelectric engine, in which we apply heat at junction 1 by immersing it in a heat reservoir $R1$ at temperature T_1, and reject heat at junction 2 by immersing it in a heat reservoir $R2$ at a lower temperature T_2. A current i flows as indicated because of the Seebeck effect. The electrical load could be a storage battery being charged by i.

Now suppose we increase the voltage E and force a reversal of current i. Equation (3-1) shows that the heat q_1 and q_2 transferred at the junctions are also reversed. Heat is absorbed from $R2$ by junction 2 and released to $R1$ by junction 1. The thermoelectric engine becomes a refrigeration engine. We see that it follows our definition of *basically reversible*.

Now we return to the block diagram of Fig. 2–8 for a basically reversible engine. The reversible conversion is accomplished by the Seebeck, Peltier, and Thomson effects; conduction of heat is an entropy-rise process on the thermal side; and i^2R loss is an entropy-rise process on the electrical side. Our first step in analyzing a machine is to apply the two laws of thermodynamics to the reversible block.

Normally, the Thomson heat is supplied by conduction from the two reservoirs. As the conduction of heat is an entropy-rise process, however, and does not belong to the reversible block, we must assume, for the purpose of analysis, that the Thomson heat is supplied by an infinite number of small heat reservoirs along the paths.

Now let us consider the energy balance of the thermal couple itself for an operating period of 1 second.

At junction 1 *the heat input is*

$$q_1 = \pi_{ab}(T_1)i \tag{3-4}$$

At junction 2, i *is from thermoelement* A *to thermoelement* B, *the heat input is*

$$q_2 = -\pi_{ab}(T_2)i \tag{3-5}$$

Let us choose the direction of increasing l as from 2 to 1. In thermal element A, the current i is in the direction of 1 to 2. Therefore,

$$q_a = -i \int_2^1 \tau_a(T) \frac{dT}{dl} dl = -i \int_{T_2}^{T_1} \tau_a(T) \, dT \tag{3-6}$$

In thermal element B, the current i is in the direction of 2 to 1. Therefore

$$q_b = i \int_{T_2}^{T_1} \tau_b(T) \, dT \tag{3-7}$$

The total Thomson heat input is

$$q_a + q_b = i \int_{T_2}^{T_1} [\tau_b(T) - \tau_a(T)] dT \tag{3-8}$$

The total heat input to the thermal couple is $\Delta Q = q_1 + q_2 + q_a + q_b$. The electrical work done is the Seebeck emf $e_{ab}(T_1, T_2)$ multiplied by the current i. As nothing is changed in the thermal couple itself after 1 second of operation, the conservation of energy requires that

$$ie_{ab}(T_1, T_2) = q_1 + q_2 + q_a + q_b \tag{3-9}$$

Substituting Eq. (3–4), Eq. (3–5), and Eq. (3–8) into Eq. (3–9) gives

$$e_{ab}(T_1, T_2) = \pi_{ab}(T_1) - \pi_{ab}(T_2) + \int_{T_2}^{T_1} [\tau_b(T) - \tau_a(T)] dT \tag{3-10}$$

Another relation can be obtained by considering the change of entropy of the total system, including the thermal couple and the heat reservoirs. Since there is no change in the thermal couple and since no entropy is involved in the doing of electrical work, the increase in entropy of the total system is equal to the sum total increase in entropy of all the thermal reservoirs. As the process is reversible, the corollary of the second law states that there is no change of entropy. Consequently,

$$\Delta S = -\frac{q_1}{T_1} - \frac{q_2}{T_2} - \int_2^1 \frac{dq_a}{T} - \int_2^1 \frac{dq_b}{T} = 0 \qquad (3\text{--}11)$$

Substituting Eq. (3–4), Eq. (3–5), and Eq. (3–8) into Eq. (3–11) gives

$$\frac{\pi_{ab}(T_1)}{T_1} - \frac{\pi_{ab}(T_2)}{T_2} + \int_{T_2}^{T_1} [\tau_b(T) - \tau_a(T)] \frac{dT}{T} = 0 \qquad (3\text{--}12)$$

Equations (3–10) and (3–12) are the two basic equations. From this point on, we need only mathematics to do the rest. Differentiating Eq. (3–10) with respect to T_1 gives

$$\frac{\partial e_{ab}(T_1, T_2)}{\partial T_1} = \frac{d\pi_{ab}(T_1)}{dT_1} - \tau_a(T_1) + \tau_b(T_1) \qquad (3\text{--}13)$$

The right-hand side of Eq. (3–13) is a function of T_1 only. Let it be denoted as $S_{ab}(T_1)$. Equation (3–13) can be written as

$$S_{ab}(T_1) \equiv \frac{d\pi_{ab}(T_1)}{dT_1} - \tau_a(T_1) + \tau_b(T_1) \qquad (3\text{--}14a)$$

$$\frac{\partial e_{ab}(T_1, T_2)}{\partial T_1} = S_{ab}(T_1) \qquad (3\text{--}14b)$$

Since Eq. (3–14a) and Eq. (3–14b) hold for any T_1, we can write T instead of T_1 in these equations. Integrating Eq. (3–14b) with respect to T from T_2 to T_1 after the change of notation gives

$$e_{ab}(T_1, T_2) - e_{ab}(T_2, T_2) = \int_{T_2}^{T_1} S_{ab}(T) \, dT$$

From symmetry considerations there can be no emf generated if the temperature difference is zero. Therefore, $e_{ab}(T_2, T_2) = 0$, and the preceding equation becomes

$$e_{ab}(T_1, T_2) = \int_{T_2}^{T_1} S_{ab}(T) \, dT \qquad (3\text{--}15)$$

If $T_1 - T_2$ is sufficiently small, Eq. (3–15) can be written as

$$e_{ab}(T_1, T_2) = (T_1 - T_2) S_{ab}(T_m) \qquad (3\text{–}16)$$

where T_m is the mean temperature $(T_1 + T_2)/2$.

The Seebeck emf is proportional to the temperature difference if the latter is small and S_{ab} is called the Seebeck coefficient.

Differentiating Eq. (3–12) gives

$$\frac{d}{dT_1}\left(\frac{\pi_{ab}(T_1)}{T_1}\right) - \frac{\tau_a(T_1) - \tau_b(T_1)}{T_1} = 0 \qquad (3\text{–}17)$$

Again, T_1 in Eq. (3–17) can simply be written as T. Since

$$\frac{d}{dT} \cdot \frac{\pi_{ab}}{T} = \frac{1}{T} \cdot \frac{d\pi_{ab}}{dT} - \frac{\pi_{ab}}{T^2}$$

Equation (3–17) can be written as

$$\frac{d\pi_{ab}}{dT} - \tau_a + \tau_b = \frac{\pi_{ab}}{T} \qquad (3\text{–}18)$$

The left-hand side of Eq. (3–18) is the right-hand side of Eq. (3–14a). Therefore,

$$S_{ab} = \frac{\pi_{ab}}{T} \qquad (3\text{–}19)$$

Equation (3–17) can be written as

$$T\frac{dS_{ab}}{dT} = \tau_a - \tau_b \qquad (3\text{–}20)$$

Equations (3–19) and (3–20) give Peltier coefficient π_{ab} and difference of Thomson coefficients $\tau_a - \tau_b$ in terms of the Seebeck coefficient S_{ab}. They are known as *Kelvin's relations*. These two equations, together with Eq. (3–15), are the basic ones for thermoelectric effects.

Example 3–1: The measured Seebeck effect between two conductors A and B in the temperature range 300°K to 800°K can be approximated by

$$S_{ab} = 2.2 \times 10^{-4} + 2 \times 10^{-6}T - 2 \times 10^{-9}T^2 - 5 \times 10^{-13}T^3$$

where S_{ab} is in volts/°K, and T is in °K. Determine the values of S_{ab}, π_{ab}, and $\tau_a - \tau_b$ at $T = 500$°K.

SOLUTION: From the given expression for S_{ab} and Eq. (3–19) and Eq. (3–20), these coefficients are calculated as:

$$S_{ab} = 0.658 \times 10^{-3} \text{ volt/}^\circ\text{K}$$

$$\pi_{ab} = 500 \times 0.658 \times 10^{-3} = 0.329 \text{ volt}$$

$$T \frac{dS_{ab}}{dT} = 2 \times 10^{-6}T - 4 \times 10^{-9}T^2 - 1.5 \times 10^{-12}T^3$$

$$\tau_a - \tau_b = 1 \times 10^{-3} - 1 \times 10^{-3} - 0.187 \times 10^{-3} = -0.187 \times 10^{-3} \text{ volt/}^\circ\text{K}$$

3-3. LAWS OF INTERMEDIATE TEMPERATURE AND INTERMEDIATE CONDUCTOR

From Eq. (3–15), it follows that

$$e_{ab}(T_1, T_2) + e_{ab}(T_2, T_3) = \int_{T_2}^{T_1} S_{ab}(T) \, dT + \int_{T_3}^{T_2} S_{ab}(T) \, dT$$

$$= \int_{T_3}^{T_1} S_{ab}(T) \, dT = e_{ab}(T_1, T_3) \qquad (3\text{--}21)$$

Equation (3–21) has the following physical significance: Let us use the same materials A and B to construct a thermal couple working between temperatures T_1, T_2, and another thermal couple working between temperatures T_2, T_3, and connect the two thermal couples in series as shown

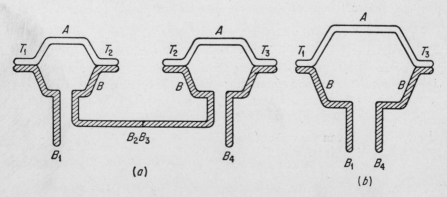

Fig. 3–3. DIAGRAMS ILLUSTRATING THE LAW OF INTERMEDIATE TEMPERATURE: (a) TWO THERMOCOUPLES CONNECTED IN SERIES; (b) THE EQUIVALENT SINGLE THERMOCOUPLE.

in Fig. 3–3(a). The total emf appearing between terminals B_1 and B_4 is exactly the same as the emf of a single thermal couple working between temperatures T_1 and T_3 as shown in Fig. 3–3(b). *This is the law of intermediate temperature.*

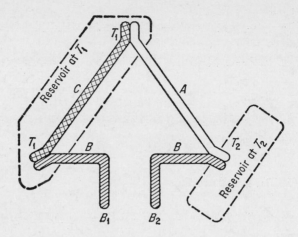

Fig. 3–4. DIAGRAM ILLUSTRATING THE LAW OF INTERMEDIATE CONDUCTOR.

Now let us consider an arrangement as shown in Fig. 3–4 where, at one end of the thermal couple, A and B are not joined directly together but through an intermediate conductor C. Thus the total heat input per second to the two junctions at T_1 is $[\pi_{ac}(T_1) + \pi_{cb}(T_1)]i$. Since there is no temperature gradient along conductor C, the Thomson heat absorbed by conductor C is zero. The same reasons leading to Eq. (3–12) give

$$\frac{\pi_{ac}(T_1) + \pi_{cb}(T_1)}{T_1} - \frac{\pi_{ab}(T_2)}{T_2} + \int_{T_2}^{T_1} [\tau_b(T) - \tau_a(T)] \frac{dT}{T} = 0$$

Subtracting the preceding equation from Eq. (3–12) gives

$$\pi_{ab}(T_1) - \pi_{ac}(T_1) - \pi_{cb}(T_1) = 0$$

Alternatively, it can be written as

$$\pi_{ab}(T) = \pi_{ac}(T) + \pi_{cb}(T) \tag{3–22}$$

It follows from Eq. (3–19) and Eq. (3–22)

$$S_{ab}(T) = S_{ac}(T) + S_{cb}(T) \tag{3–23}$$

Equations (3–22) and (3–23) are known as the *law of intermediate conductor*. They have some very significant practical implications which will be discussed below:

Basic Construction of Thermoelectric Engine. As conduction of heat directly from R1 to R2 through the thermal elements causes a loss of useful energy, it is to be avoided as much as possible. Good thermoelectric materials are usually poor conductors of heat. This means that with two good thermoelectric materials joined together directly, it becomes a problem to conduct heat to the junction without causing appreciable temperature drop. Because of the law of intermediate conductor, we can use a good conducting material, say, copper, as the conductor C of Fig. 3–4. Heat can be conducted from copper to the two junctions, without appreciable temperature drop, yet thermoelectrically it is still the same as joining A and B directly together. The arrangement of such a thermal couple is shown in Fig. 3–5. Heat is conducted to, and from, the junctions through copper blocks at both ends.

Measurements of Seebeck and Peltier Coefficients. Because of Eq. (3–22) and Eq. (3–23), π_{ab} and S_{ab} can be written as

$$\pi_{ab}(T) = \pi_a(T) - \pi_b(T) \tag{3-24}$$

$$S_{ab}(T) = S_a(T) - S_b(T) \tag{3-25}$$

where $\pi_a(T)$ and $S_a(T)$ are coefficients of material A relative to some neutral metal. $S_a(T)$ is also called the *thermoelectric power* of A. To determine $\pi_{ab}(T)$ or $S_{ab}(T)$ for N different materials, we need only measure $N - 1$ values of $\pi_{a1}(T)$, or $S_{a1}(T)$ where $a = 2, 3, \ldots, N$. The Peltier coefficient π_{ab} between any materials a and b can be calculated as

$$\pi_{ab}(T) = \pi_a(T) - \pi_b(T) = \pi_{a1}(T) - \pi_{b1}(T) \tag{3-26}$$

A similar relation holds for $S_{ab}(T)$. Without the law of intermediate conductors, we would need $N(N - 1)/2$ measurements to determine the Peltier or Seebeck coefficients for all possible combinations of materials.

3-4. ENTROPY ASSOCIATED WITH CHARGE CARRIERS

A more abstract idea is to regard $S_a(T)$ as the entropy per unit charge of charge carriers in material A at temperature T.

Equations (3–19) and (3–20) can be written as

$$S_a(T) - S_b(T) = \frac{\pi_{ab}(T)}{T} \tag{3-27}$$

$$\frac{dS_a}{dT} = \frac{\tau_a}{T} \tag{3-28}$$

Equation (3–27) means that as heat $\pi_{ab}(T)$ is absorbed by the charge carriers at the junction, their entropy is increased by π_{ab}/T.

Equation (3–28) means that as the charge carriers travel from a temperature T to a temperature $T + \Delta T$, they absorb an amount of heat $\tau_a \Delta T$, and their entropy is increased by $\tau_a \Delta T / T$.

Equation (3–25) now has a new significance:

The Seebeck coefficient $S_{ab}(T)$ *is the difference in entropies* $S_a(T) - S_b(T)$ *of one unit charge of charge carriers in the two materials at temperature* T.

3-5. THE BASIC THERMOELECTRIC ENGINE

Let us consider the basic thermoelectric engine of Fig. 3–5. Heat is transferred to the elements A and B through the copper block on top, and the rejected heat is dissipated to the surroundings through the two copper blocks at the bottom. The latter also serve as the electrical terminals on which the load is connected. In general, the transfer of heat between the side surface of a thermal element and its surrounding is quite negligible, and we shall *assume that the transfer of heat takes place at the two ends only.*

In addition to the reversible effects there are two other important effects:

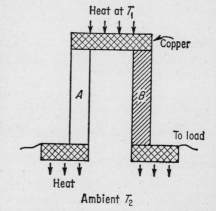

Fig. 3–5. Actual Arrangement of a Basic Thermoelectric Engine, Utilizing the Law of Intermediate Conductor.

(1) Heat is conducted from reservoir R1 to reservoir R2 at the rate of

$$q_c = k(T_1 - T_2) \tag{3-29}$$

where k is the total thermal conductance of the elements A and B.

(2) There is an i^2R loss due to the series resistance R of the two thermal elements. Since the i^2R loss is uniformly distributed along the thermal elements, half of the heat so generated is conducted to R1 and half of the heat so generated is conducted to R2. The effects of the i^2R loss are

    (a) The terminal voltage becomes

$$V_{ab} = e_{ab} - iR$$

    (b) Heat is conducted into the two reservoirs at the rate of $q_r/2$ each, where $q_r = i^2R$.

Among the reversible effects, the Thomson heat is supplied by conduction from the two reservoirs. The exact quota of the Thomson heat supplied by each reservoir depends on the temperature gradient and variations of τ_a and τ_b with T. It is not easy to calculate without making some simplifying assumptions. A useful approximation is that $q_T/2$ is supplied by each reservoir, where

$$q_T = \int_{T_2}^{T_1} (\tau_b - \tau_a)\, dT \tag{3-30}$$

Summarizing the foregoing, the rate of thermal input from $R1$ to the thermoelectric generator is

$$Q_1' = q_1 + q_c - \frac{q_r}{2} + \frac{q_T}{2} = \pi_{ab}(T_1)i + k(T_1 - T_2)$$

$$- \frac{i^2R}{2} + \frac{i}{2}\int_{T_2}^{T_1} (\tau_b - \tau_a)\, dT \tag{3-31}$$

The rate of heat dissipated into $R2$ is

$$Q_2' = -q_2 + q_c + \frac{q_r}{2} - \frac{q_T}{2} = \pi_{ab}(T_2)i + k(T_1 - T_2)$$

$$+ \frac{i^2R}{2} - \frac{i}{2}\int_{T_2}^{T_1} (\tau_b - \tau_a)\, dT \tag{3-32}$$

The output electric power is

$$W' = Q_1' - Q_2' = i\left[\pi_{ab}(T_1) - \pi_{ab}(T_2) + \int_{T_2}^{T_1} (\tau_b - \tau_a)\, dT - iR\right]$$

$$\tag{3-33}$$

Using Eq. (3-10), Eq. (3-33) is reduced to

$$W' = [e_{ab}(T_1, T_2) - iR]i = V_0 i \qquad (3-34)$$

as it should be.

For refrigeration operation, the signs of i, W, and Q are reversed. Equations (3-32) and (3-33) become

$$Q_2'' = \pi_{ab}(T_2)i - k(T_1 - T_2) - \frac{i^2 R}{2} - \frac{i}{2}\int_{T_2}^{T_1}(\tau_b - \tau_a)\,dT \qquad (3-35)$$

$$W'' = [e_{ab}(T_1, T_2) + iR]i = Vi \qquad (3-36)$$

3-6. APPROXIMATE EQUATIONS FOR ENGINES WITH $T_1 - T_2 < T_2$

Equations (3-31) to (3-36) are general enough and are good for performance calculations. They can be simplified for the important special case of small $T_1 - T_2$ relative to the mean temperature $T_m = (T_1 + T_2)/2$.

The Equivalent Peltier Effect. Because of the assumption that transfer of heat takes place only at the two ends of the thermal elements, the Peltier and Thomson effects can be lumped together. Let $\overline{q_1}$ and $\overline{q_2}$ denote the total heat transferred *into* the junctions owing to the two reversible effects. Then

$$\overline{q_1} \equiv q_1 + \frac{q_T}{2}$$

$$\overline{q_2} \equiv q_2 + \frac{q_T}{2} \qquad (3-37)$$

Equations (3-20) and (3-30) give

$$\frac{q_T}{i} = -\int_{T_2}^{T_1} T\frac{dS_{ab}}{dT}\,dT = -TS_{ab}\Big|_{T_2}^{T_1} + \int_{T_2}^{T_1} S_{ab}\,dT$$

$$= T_2 S_{ab}(T_2) - T_1 S_{ab}(T_1) + (T_1 - T_2)S_m \qquad (3-38)$$

where S_m is the average Seebeck coefficient in the temperature range of interest:

$$S_m \equiv \frac{1}{T_1 - T_2}\int_{T_2}^{T_1} S_{ab}(T)\,dT \qquad (3-39)$$

Equations (3-37) and (3-38) can be combined to give:

$$\frac{\bar{q}_1}{i} = \frac{1}{2} \left[T_1 S_{ab}(T_1) + T_2 S_{ab}(T_2) + (T_1 - T_2) S_m \right] = T_1 S_m + \frac{\Delta}{2} \quad (3\text{-}40)$$

Similarly,

$$\frac{\bar{q}_2}{i} = T_2 S_m + \frac{\Delta}{2} \quad (3\text{-}41)$$

where

$$\Delta = T_1 [S_{ab}(T_1) - S_m] + T_2 [S_{ab}(T_2) - S_m] \quad (3\text{-}42)$$

Subtracting Eq. (3-41) from Eq. (3-40) yields

$$\bar{q}_1 - \bar{q}_2 = (T_1 - T_2) S_m i \quad (3\text{-}43)$$

Equations (3-40), (3-41), and (3-43) have an interesting significance. If $\Delta = 0$, Eq. (3-40) and Eq. (3-41) would give

$$\frac{\bar{q}_1}{\bar{q}_2} = \frac{T_1}{T_2}$$

which is characteristic of a reversible process. The quantity Δ, therefore, represents the irreversible effect of conduction of Thomson heat to the two ends. It is not exact because we have assumed that the Thomson heat is conducted in equal amounts to both ends, but in reality the partition depends on the distribution of the Thomson heat along the thermoelectric elements and is not equal.

For sufficiently small $T_1 - T_2$, Δ is a negligible quantity, as is shown below:

Let $T_m = (T_1 + T_2)/2$. The function $S_{ab}(T)$ can be expressed as a power series of $T - T_m$:

$$S_{ab}(T) = a_0 + a_1(T - T_m) + a_2(T - T_m)^2 + \cdots \quad (3\text{-}44)$$

Substituting Eq. (3-44) into Eq. (3-39) and integrating gives

$$S_m = a_0 + \frac{a_2}{3} (T_1 - T_m)^2 + \cdots \quad (3\text{-}45)$$

Substituting Eq. (3-44) and Eq. (3-45) into Eq. (3-42) gives

$$\Delta = \frac{a_1}{2} (T_1 - T_2)^2 + \frac{a_2}{6} (T_1 + T_2)(T_1 - T_2)^2 + \cdots \quad (3\text{-}46)$$

The higher-order terms in Eq. (3-44) and Eq. (3-45) can contribute only to terms of third or higher power in $T_1 - T_2$.

Equation (3–46) illustrates that Δ is of the order $(T_1 - T_2)^2$. When $T_1 - T_2$ is sufficiently small, $\Delta/2$ is negligible compared to $\bar{q}_1$ and $\bar{q}_2$. Therefore,

$$\bar{q}_1 \cong T_1 S_m i$$

$$\bar{q}_2 \cong T_2 S_m i \tag{3-47}$$

The combined Peltier and Thomson effects operating between two temperatures T_1 and T_2 of relatively small $T_1 - T_2$ is approximately equivalent to a Peltier effect alone, with a constant Seebeck coefficient equal to S_m. The equivalent Peltier effect obeys the relation that

$$\frac{\bar{q}_1}{T_1} = \frac{\bar{q}_2}{T_2} = S_m i$$

In practice, the equivalence just cited is found to hold quite well for a value of $T_1 - T_2$ less than, or equal to, T_m.

Performance Calculations. Using the approximate equations (3–47), the operating equations for a thermoelectric generator can be readily obtained.

Heat Input

$$Q'_1 = \quad T_1 S_m i \quad + \quad k(T_1 - T_2) \quad - \quad \frac{i^2 R}{2} \tag{3-48}$$

$$\text{Peltier + Thomson} \qquad \text{conduction} \qquad \text{copper loss}$$

Rejected Heat

$$Q'_2 = T_2 S_m i + k(T_1 - T_2) + \frac{i^2 R}{2} \tag{3-49}$$

Electrical Output

$$W' = Q'_1 - Q'_2 = [(T_1 - T_2) S_m - iR]i = Vi \tag{3-50}$$

where V is the output voltage

$$V = (T_1 - T_2) S_m - iR \tag{3-51}$$

Equation (3–51) means that the output characteristics of a thermoelectric generator with fixed junction temperatures are the same as that of a battery with an electromotive force $(T_1 - T_2) S_m$ and an internal resistance R.

For a refrigeration engine, the signs of Q_1, Q_2, W, and i are reversed.

The corresponding equations are

$$Q''_1 = T_1 S_m i - k(T_1 - T_2) + \frac{i^2 R}{2} \qquad (3\text{-}52)$$

$$Q''_2 = T_2 S_m i - k(T_1 - T_2) - \frac{i^2 R}{2} \qquad (3\text{-}53)$$

$$W'' = (T_1 - T_2) S_m i + i^2 R \qquad (3\text{-}54)$$

$$V = (T_1 - T_2) S_m + i R \qquad (3\text{-}55)$$

Example 3-2: Certain elements A and B have the following properties in the temperature range of interest:

$$S_m = 0.003 \text{ volt/}^\circ\text{K}$$

thermal conductance of *each* element = 0.04 watt/$^\circ$K

resistance of *each* element = 0.025 ohm

The elements operate between junction temperature of 1250°K and 750°K. Determine

(a) Maximum output and efficiency at maximum output
(b) Input power and terminal voltage at no load
(c) Input power and current under short-circuit condition

SOLUTION: The generated emf is

$$E = 0.003 \times (1250 - 750) = 1.5 \text{ volts}$$

The internal resistance is

$$R = 0.025 \text{ ohm} \times 2 = 0.05 \text{ ohm}$$

$$k = 0.04 \text{ watt/}^\circ\text{K} \times 2 = 0.08 \text{ watt/}^\circ\text{K}$$

(a) $$W_{\max} = \frac{E^2}{4R} = 11.25 \text{ watts}$$

$$i = \frac{E}{2R} = 15 \text{ amp}$$

$$Q'_1 = 1250 \times 0.003 \times 15 + 40 - \frac{15^2 \times 0.05}{2}$$

$$= 56.25 + 40 - 5.62 = 90.63 \text{ watts}$$

$$\eta = 11.25/90.63 = 12.4\%$$

(b) At no load

$$V_1 = E = 1.5 \text{ volts}$$

$$Q_1 = k(T_1 - T_2) = 0.08 \times 500 = 40 \text{ watts}$$

(c) Under short-circuit condition

$$i = \frac{E}{R} = 30 \text{ amp}$$

$$Q_1' = 1250 \times 0.003 \times 30 + 0.08 \times 500 - \frac{30^2 \times 0.05}{2}$$

$$= 112.5 + 40 - 22.5 = 130 \text{ watts}$$

Operating Point at Maximum Efficiency. Since efficiency is one of the most important factors in determining whether power-generating equipment is feasible, thermoelectric generators are usually designed to operate at, or near, the maximum efficiency. From Eq. (3–48) and Eq. (3–50), the thermal efficiency can be written as

$$\eta = \frac{W'}{Q_1'} = \frac{(T_1 - T_2)S_m i - i^2 R}{T_1 S_m i + k(T_1 - T_2) - i^2 R/2} \tag{3-56}$$

In Eq. (3–56), it is obvious that if i is too small, the conduction term will predominate. If i is too large, the $i^2 R$ term will predominate. In order to obtain maximum efficiency there is an optimum value for i. Let M denote the ratio of useful output voltage to the iR drop

$$M = \frac{(T_1 - T_2)S_m - iR}{iR} \tag{3-57}$$

Then, $iR = (T_1 - T_2)S_m/(1 + M)$. Dividing the denominator and numerator of the right-hand side of Eq. (3–56) by $i^2 R$, the numerator becomes M, and the denominator becomes

$$\frac{T_1(1 + M)}{T_1 - T_2} + \frac{kR(1 + M)^2}{S_m{}^2(T_1 - T_2)} - \frac{1}{2}$$

Let z denote $S_m{}^2/kR$. Equation (3–56) can be rewritten as

$$\frac{W'}{Q_1'} = \frac{T_1 - T_2}{T_1} \cdot \frac{M}{i + M + (1 + M)^2/T_1 z - \frac{1}{2} \cdot [(T_1 - T_2)/T_1]}$$

$$= \frac{T_1 - T_2}{T_1} \cdot \frac{1}{F(M)} \tag{3-58}$$

where

$$F(M) = 1 + \frac{2}{T_1 z} + \frac{M}{T_1 z} + \frac{1}{M}\left(\frac{1}{2} \cdot \frac{T_1 + T_2}{T_1} + \frac{1}{T_1 z}\right) \quad (3\text{–}59)$$

The lowest value of $F(M)$ is obtained if

$$M = M_0 = \sqrt{1 + T_m z} = \sqrt{1 + T_m S_m{}^2/kR} \quad (3\text{–}60)$$

$$F(M_0) = 1 + \frac{2}{T_1 z} + \frac{2M_0}{T_1 z} = 1 + \frac{2(1 + M_0)}{T_1 z}$$

$$= 1 + \frac{2T_m}{T_1(M_0 - 1)} = \frac{T_1 M_0 + T_2}{T_1(M_0 - 1)} \quad (3\text{–}61)$$

The optimum thermal efficiency is

$$\eta_0 = \frac{T_1 - T_2}{T_1} \cdot \frac{M_0 - 1}{M_0 + T_2/T_1} \quad (3\text{–}62)$$

For refrigeration operation, Eq. (3–53) and Eq. (3–54) give

$$C \equiv \frac{Q_2''}{W''} = \frac{T_2 S_m i - k(T_1 - T_2) - (i^2 R/2)}{i(T_1 - T_2)S_m + i^2 R} \quad (3\text{–}63)$$

Let M denote the ratio of applied voltage to iR drop. Equation (3–63) becomes

$$C = \frac{T_2}{T_1 - T_2} \cdot \left[1 + \frac{2}{T_2 z} - \frac{1}{M}\left(\frac{T_m}{T_2} + \frac{1}{T_2 z}\right) - \frac{M}{T_2 z}\right] \quad (3\text{–}64)$$

In order to obtain the highest coefficient of performance, the optimum value of M is again

$$M_0 = \sqrt{1 + T_m z}$$

The optimum coefficient of performance is

$$C_0 = \frac{T_2}{T_1 - T_2}\left[1 + \frac{2}{T_2 z} - \frac{2M_0}{T_2 z}\right] = \frac{T_2}{T_1 - T_2} \cdot \frac{M_0 - T_1/T_2}{M_0 + 1} \quad (3\text{–}65)$$

3-7. FIGURE OF MERIT

The preceding section shows that the optimum performance of a thermo-electric engine depends on the ratio $T_m S_m{}^2/kR$. The higher this ratio is, the better will be the performance. Now T_m is fixed by the design condition.

S_m is fixed by the choice of materials. For any combination of materials, the dimensions of the thermal elements should be so selected that kR is a minimum. Let

K_a, K_b = thermal conductivities of A and B, respectively,

ρ_a, ρ_b = electrical resistivities of A and B, respectively,

L_a, L_b = lengths of the thermal elements,

σ_a, σ_b = cross-sectional areas of the thermal elements.

The thermal conductance k and electrical resistance R can be calculated from the foregoing data:

$$k = \frac{\sigma_a K_a}{L_a} + \frac{\sigma_b K_b}{L_b} \tag{3-66}$$

$$R = \frac{L_a \rho_a}{\sigma_a} + \frac{L_b \rho_b}{\sigma_b} \tag{3-67}$$

Let r denote the ratio $\sigma_a L_b / \sigma_b L_a$. From Eq. (3-66) and Eq. (3-67)

$$kR = (rK_a + K_b)\left(\frac{\rho_a}{r} + \rho_b\right) = \rho_a k_a + \rho_b K_b + rK_a \rho_b + \frac{1}{r} K_b \rho_a \tag{3-68}$$

Therefore, kR is a minimum if

$$r = \sqrt{\frac{K_b \rho_a}{K_a \rho_b}} \tag{3-69}$$

and Eq. (3-68) becomes

$$(kR)_0 = \rho_a K_a + \rho_b K_b + 2\sqrt{K_a K_b \rho_a \rho_b} = (\sqrt{\rho_a K_a} + \sqrt{\rho_b K_b})^2$$

The constant

$$\theta \equiv \frac{T S_{ab}^2}{(kR)_0} = \frac{T S_{ab}^2}{(\sqrt{\rho_a K_a} + \sqrt{\rho_b K_b})^2} \tag{3-70}$$

is called the *figure of merit* for the combination of materials A and B.

In Soviet literature, the parameter

$$z_a = \frac{S_a^2}{K_a \rho_a} \tag{3-71}$$

is used to indicate the merit of material A. There is increasing adaptation of this definition of the figure of merit in the United States literature. There appears to be little scientific reason, however, to prefer Eq. (3-71) over Eq. (3-70) since both parameters z and θ are temperature dependent. The parameter θ is dimensionless and also gives a direct indication of the performance, but there are more data in terms of z. Both z and θ will be used in this text.

For studying materials, it is convenient to define a figure of merit for a single material:

$$\theta_a = \frac{T S_a^2}{K_a \rho_a} \tag{3-72}$$

Suppose that the material B has the same K and ρ as A, and $S_a = -S_b$. Then $S_{ab} = 2S_a$ and $\theta = \theta_a$.

The relative efficiency η_{rel} and relative coefficient of performance C_{rel} are defined as the actual quantities over the corresponding Carnot values. From Eq. (3–62) and Eq. (3–65),

$$\eta_{rel} \equiv \frac{\eta}{\eta_{Carnot}} = \frac{M_0 - 1}{M_0 + T_2/T_1} \tag{3-73}$$

$$C_{rel} \equiv \frac{C}{C_{Carnot}} = \frac{M_0 - T_1/T_2}{M_0 + 1} \tag{3-74}$$

where $M_0 = \sqrt{1 + \theta_m}$, and θ_m is the value of θ as calculated from mean values of S, K, and ρ in the temperature range between T_1 and T_2. The values of η_{rel} and C_{rel} versus θ are plotted in Fig. 3–6 and Fig. 3–7 respectively. Note that, with a figure of merit of 3 or higher, thermoelectric engines would become commercially competitive. The highest figure of merit of known materials is about 1. As this is already many times better than what was known a decade ago, the future of thermoelectric generators and refrigerators is bright indeed.

3-8. PROPERTIES OF THERMOELECTRIC MATERIALS

The discussion in Sec. 3–7 points out the three pertinent properties of a thermoelectric material: the Seebeck coefficient S, the thermal conductivity K, and the electrical resistivity ρ. The best material has large S, and low values for K and ρ. These three properties are not unrelated, however. For solids, the general tendency of change of ρ, K, and S as the density of charge carriers varies is shown in Fig. 3–8.

In Fig. 3–8(a), S is the thermoelectric power of the material relative to a neutral metal. We note two significant points:

(1) The thermoelectric power is positive for p-type material and negative for n-type material. This means that if p-type materials formed into a

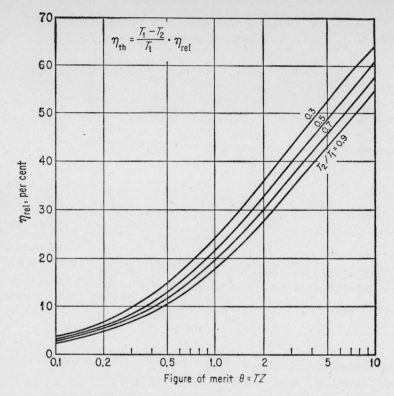

Fig. 3–6. MAXIMUM RELATIVE EFFICIENCY VERSUS THE FIGURE OF MERIT OF THE ELEMENTS.

thermal couple with neutral metal, positive current will flow from the p-type material into the neutral metal at the cold junction.

(2) After the peak, the absolute value of S decreases as the density of charge carriers increases.

In Fig. 3–8(b), both the thermal conductivity K and electrical conductivity $1/\rho$ increase almost linearly with the density of charge carriers. The conduction of electricity is entirely due to the charge carriers and $1/\rho$ becomes zero as the density vanishes. But the conduction of heat is partly owing to lattice vibration and only partly due to conveying action of the charge carriers. The former effect accounts for K_L; the latter effect accounts for the rising value of K as the number of charge carriers is increased.

From Fig. 3–8(a) and (b), it is obvious that, as the density of charge carriers is increased, the figure of merit first rises and then decreases. The maximum value of θ occurs at a density of about 10^{19} per cubic centimeter

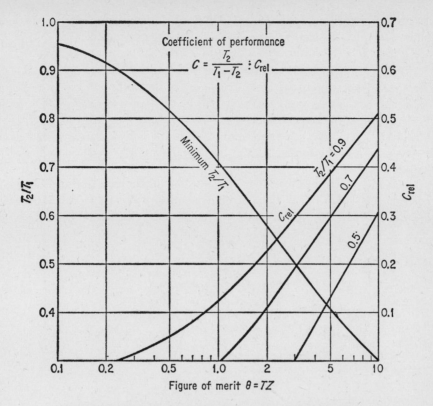

Fig. 3-7. Maximum Relative Coefficient of Performance versus the Figure of Merit of the Elements.

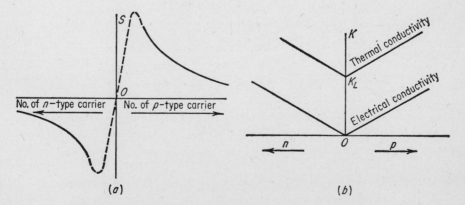

Fig. 3-8. Seebeck Coefficient and Conductivities of a Semiconductor versus Concentration of Impurities.

and is about a thousand times smaller than the density of charge carriers in pure metals. One can thus conclude that the best thermoelectric materials are likely to be found among semiconductors and semimetals.

One example of such a semiconductor is the lead telluride compound, Pb Te. It is not among the best, which are known today, in terms of figure of merit, but it has been used for thermoelectric generation for several years and its properties are fairly well known. The materials can be doped with sodium to form a p-type conductor or Pb I_2 to form an n-type conductor. As Na has fewer valence electrons than Pb, replacement of Pb atom by Na atom increases the number of holes. Similarly substitution of a Te atom increases the number of electrons. Thus, by changing the composition, the type and density of charge carriers can be modified at will. Figures 3–9 to 3–13 show the Seebeck coefficient, electrical resistivity, and

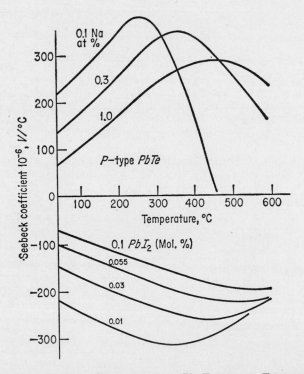

Fig. 3–9. SEEBECK COEFFICIENT OF Pb Te VERSUS TEMPERATURE. (Reprinted from R. W. Fritts, "Design Parameters for Optimizing the Efficiency of Thermoelectric Generators Utilizing P-Type and N-Type Lead Telluride" *AIEE Transactions*, Vol. **78**, 1959, Part I.)

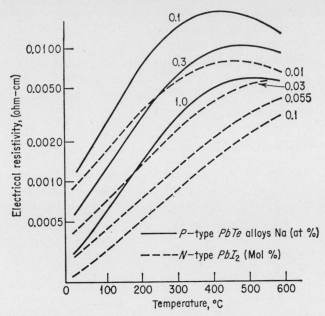

Fig. 3–10. RESISTIVITY OF Pb Te VERSUS TEMPERATURE. (Reprinted from R. W. Fritts, "Design Parameters for Optimizing the Efficiency of Thermoelectric Generators Utilizing P-Type and N-Type Lead Telluride" *AIEE Transactions*, V9l. **78**, 1959, Part I.)

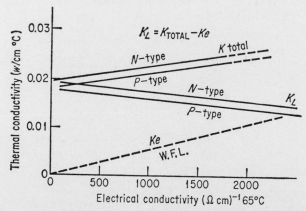

Fig. 3–11. THERMAL CONDUCTIVITY VERSUS TEMPERATURE. (Reprinted from R. W. Fritts, "Design Parameters for Optimizing the Efficiency of Thermoelectric Generators Utilizing P-Type and N-Type Lead Telluride" *AIEE Transactions*, Vol. **78**, 1959, Part I.)

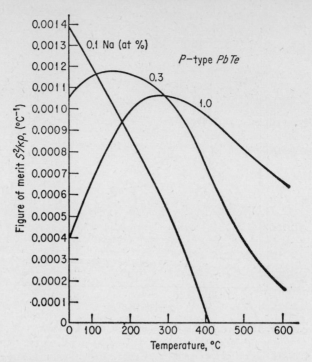

Fig. 3–12. FIGURE OF MERIT OF p-TYPE Pb Te VERSUS TEM-
PERATURE.   (Reprinted from R. W. Fritts, "Design Parameters
for Optimizing the Efficiency of Thermoelectric Generators
Utilizing P-Type and N-Type Lead Telluride" *AIEE Transactions*, Vol. **78**, 1959, Part I.)

$S^2/K\rho$ as functions of temperature and amount of doping. We note the
following:

Seebeck coefficient

1. The Seebeck coefficient rises to a maximum and then declines as temperature increases. The peak is higher and occurs at a lower temperature
for compounds with less doping.

2. At low temperature, the Seebeck coefficient of a material with a relatively low percentage of doping is highest. At high temperatures, the Seebeck coefficient of a material with a high percentage of doping is highest.

3. The crossover occurs much sooner for the p-type Pb Te than for the
n-type Pb Te.

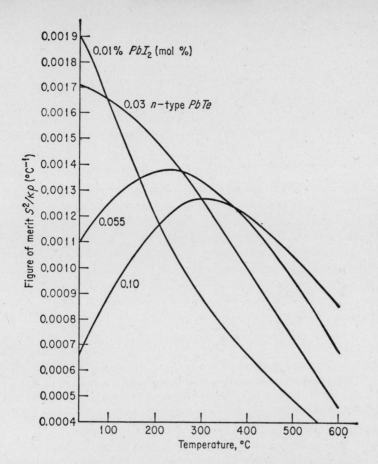

Fig. 3–13. Figure of Merit of n-Type Pb Te versus Temperature. (Reprinted from R. W. Fritts, "Design Parameters for Optimizing the Efficiency of Thermoelectric Generators Utilizing P-Type and N-Type Lead Telluride" *AIEE Transactions*, Vol. **78**, 1959, Part I.)

Electrical resistivity

1. The resistivities of both types of materials tend to rise with temperature at lower temperatures and to decline at higher temperatures.

2. The z values of both types of material show the same tendencies of variation as the thermoelectric power.

3-9. TYPICAL LAYOUTS OF THERMOELECTRIC ENGINES

The layouts of thermoelectric engines are designed on two considerations:

(1) The thermal and electrical impedances must match those of the source and the load.

(2) The conduction of heat not inherent to the device is kept at a minimum.

Since the thermoelectric materials usually have low voltage, high current, and fairly low thermal conductivity, the elements are usually in series electrically but in parallel thermally. Some such layouts are shown in Figs. 3-14(a), (b), and (c). In Fig. 3-14(a), the thermal elements are spaced along the length of the fuel chamber. This layout is more suitable to long fuel chambers with small diameter. In Fig. 3-14(b), the thermal elements are spaced radially. This layout is more suitable to short fuel chambers with large diameter. In Fig. 3-14(c), the thermal elements are arranged in a two-dimensional array. In all cases, we see that the electrical leads are always taken from the ambient temperature side, to reduce the loss of thermal energy or refrigeration capacity by conduction through the electrical leads.

The source of heat for a thermoelectric generator may be either conventional fuel or nuclear fuel. We note that the shape of the fuel chamber of Fig. 3-14(a) suits a nuclear fuel element neatly.

If a positive current is set into the negative terminal by an external source of emf, the thermoelectric generator becomes a refrigeration engine and the fuel chamber becomes a refrigerated compartment.

For temperature regulation, one need only replace the battery by a source of varying emf. When the direction of current is reversed, the direction of heat transfer is also reversed. Thus, the thermoelectric engine can be readily used for bidirectional temperature regulation.

Sometimes, a large temperature difference is desired; then one can use the two-stage design as shown in Fig. 3-15. The first thermal couple cools from T_1 to some intermediate temperature T_3, and the second thermal couple cools from T_3 to the final temperature T_2. The heat released by the second thermal couple is absorbed by the first thermal couple. Multistage design, however, is rarely used in thermoelectric generators. The reason for this difference is illustrated by Eq. (3-73) and Eq. (3-74): The relative efficiency η_{rel} increases as the ratio T_1/T_2 is increased, but C_{rel} decreases as T_1/T_2 is increased. As a matter of fact, given any θ_m, the temperature ratio is limited by

$$\frac{T_1}{T_2} \leq \sqrt{1 + \theta_m}$$

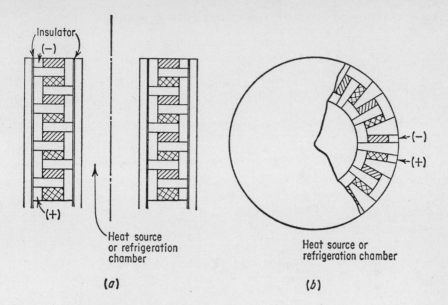

Thermoelectrically positive material

Thermoelectrically negative material

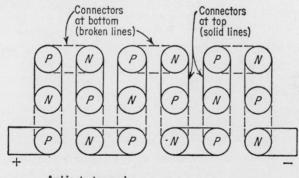

Ambient: top end

Heat source: bottom end

Fig. 3–14. Typical Arrangements of Thermoelectric Elements: (a) Longitudinal Array; (b) Radial Array; (c) Two Dimensional Array.

Whenever the equality sign in the foregoing equation is reached, Eq. (3–74) shows that the cooling effect is zero. The advantage of multistaging is that the temperature ratio T_1/T_2 can be extended. There is no theoretical limitation to the number of stages as long as there is material available for

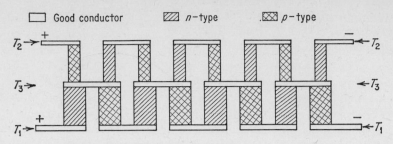

Fig. 3-15. CASCADING OF A THERMOELECTRIC ENGINE.

working in the various temperature ranges. But practically speaking, the input power requirement increases exponentially with the number of stages, and a limit of economic feasibility is soon reached. These points are made quantitative in Prob. 3-7, Prob. 3-8, and Prob. 3-9.

3-10. DESIGN OF THERMOELECTRIC GENERATORS AND HEAT PUMPS

Thermoelectric generators and heat pumps (or refrigeration engines) are usually designed for optimum efficiency at the nominal operating point. The given conditions of design are

1. Operating temperatures, T_1 and T_2
2. Terminal voltage V
3. Output capacity, which is W' for a generator, Q_1'' for a heat pump, or Q_2'' for a refrigeration engine.

The first step in design is choosing the type of material to use, dope concentration, possibility of multistaging in the case of a heat pump or a refrigeration engine, etc. As this step in design is dominated by economics, availability of material, and space, etc., rather than by scientific considerations, it is bypassed in this book.

At the second step, the problem is already reduced to that of designing a single-stage engine with T_1, T_2, V, S_m, ρ, K, and W' (or Q_1'' or Q_2'') given. The number of couples in series and sizes of the elements are to be determined.

One significant point about the equations developed in Sec. 3-6 and Sec. 3-7 is that if the four parameters L_a, L_b, σ_a, and σ_b are changed in proportion, the performance of the thermoelectric engine is not changed at all. Thus the dimensions cannot be determined from these equations alone and an auxiliary condition is needed.

We recall that, in deriving the equations of Sec. 3–6 and Sec. 3–7, we have completely neglected the thermal and electrical resistances at the junctions between the copper block and the thermoelectric elements. To be sure, with thermoelectric elements of sufficient size, junction resistances are negligible. This is not true, however, when we allow the sizes to shrink to zero. A minimum length of the thermoelectric elements of about 0.5–1 cm, or a maximum current density is generally specified. With the auxiliary condition, the equations developed in Sec. 3–6 and Sec. 3–7 are sufficient to specify everything. Step-by-step procedures are given below to illustrate this point:

Generator Design

1. Given values are T_1, T_2, V, W', K_a, K_b, ρ_a, ρ_b, S_m, L_a, and L_b.

2. Calculate

$$\theta_m = \frac{(T_1 + T_2) S_m^2}{2(\sqrt{\rho_a K_a} + \sqrt{\rho_b K_b})^2}$$

3. Calculate

$$M_0 = \sqrt{1 + \theta_m}$$

4. Calculate voltage per couple

$$V_1 = (T_1 - T_2) S_m \cdot \frac{M_0}{1 + M_0}$$

5. Number of couples in series

$$N_s \geq \frac{V}{V_1}$$

N_s is the smallest integer satisfying the foregoing inequality.

6. Calculate operating current

$$i = \frac{W'}{V}$$

7. Calculate total resistance per couple

$$R = V_1/iM_0$$

8. Calculate the optimum value of the ratio r:

$$r = \sqrt{\frac{K_b \rho_a}{K_a \rho_b}}$$

9. Equation (3–67) gives

$$R = \frac{L_a}{\sigma_a} (\rho_a + r\rho_b)$$

Therefore, L_a/σ_a can be calculated as

$$\frac{L_a}{\sigma_a} = \frac{R}{(\rho_a + r\rho_b)}$$

10. Calculate the areas of the elements

$$\sigma_a = \frac{L_a}{(L_a/\sigma_a)}$$

$$\sigma_b = \frac{L_b}{r(L_a/\sigma_a)}$$

11. The thermal conductance k can be calculated as

$$k = \frac{1}{R} (\sqrt{\rho_a K_a} + \sqrt{\rho_b K_b})^2$$

If the allowed current densities J_a and J_b are given instead of the lengths of elements, the tenth step is replaced by

$$\sigma_a = \frac{i}{J_a}, \qquad \sigma_b = \frac{i}{J_b}$$

$$L_a = \sigma_a \left(\frac{L_a}{\sigma_a}\right), \qquad L_b = r\sigma_b \left(\frac{L_a}{\sigma_a}\right)$$

If L_a and L_b are required to be equal, the larger of the two values is used for both L_a and L_b, and the area is changed proportionately.

Heat Pump or Refrigeration Engine Design

1. Given values are T_1, T_2, V, Q_1'' or Q_2'', K_a, K_b, ρ_a, ρ_b, S_m, L_a, and L_b (or J_a and J_b).

2. Calculate θ_m.

3. Calculate M_0.

4. Calculate voltage per couple

$$V_1 = (T_1 - T_2) S_m \frac{M_0}{M_0 - 1}$$

5. Number of couples in series

$$N_s \leq \frac{V}{V_1}$$

N_s is the largest integer satisfying the preceding inequality.

6. Calculate input watts and operating current:

$$C_0 = \frac{T_2 M_0 - T_1}{(T_1 - T_2)(M_0 + 1)}$$

$$W'' = \frac{Q_1''}{C_0 + 1} \qquad \left(\text{or } W'' = \frac{Q_2''}{C} \right)$$

$$i = \frac{W''}{V}$$

7. Calculate total resistance per couple

$$R = \frac{V_1}{iM_0}$$

The rest of the design calculations are identical with the generator calculations.

The third step is performance calculation as a final check.

Example 3–3: Design a thermoelectric generator to operate from a heat source of 1000°K and to reject heat at 600°K. The required output is 50 watts at 6 volts. The properties of the materials to be used are

$$S_m = 0.001 \text{ volt/°K}$$

$$K_a = 0.03 \text{ watt/cm-°K}$$

$$K_b = 0.02 \text{ watt/cm-°K}$$

$$\rho_a = 0.005 \text{ ohm-cm}$$

$$\rho_b = 0.006 \text{ ohm-cm}$$

Assume the thermoelectric elements to be 1 cm in length.

SOLUTION: The design calculations are done as outlined:

2. $\sqrt{\rho_a K_a} + \sqrt{\rho_b K_b} = 0.01225 + 0.01095 = 0.0232$

$T_m = \frac{1}{2}(1000 + 600) = 800°\text{K}$

$$\theta_m = \frac{800 \times 10^{-6}}{2.32^2 \times 10^{-4}} = 1.49$$

3. $M_0 = \sqrt{2.49} = 1.58$

4. $V_1 = 400 \times 0.001 \times \dfrac{1.58}{2.58} = 0.245$ volt/couple

5. $\dfrac{V}{V_1} = \dfrac{6}{0.245} = 24.5$

$N_s = 25$

6. $i = 50/6 = 8.33$ amp

7. $R = \dfrac{0.245}{8.33 \times 1.58} = 0.0186$ ohm

8. $r = \sqrt{\dfrac{0.02 \times 0.005}{0.03 \times 0.006}} = \sqrt{\dfrac{1}{1.8}} = 0.746$

9. $\dfrac{L_a}{\sigma_a} = \dfrac{0.0186}{0.005 + 0.00447} = \dfrac{0.0186}{0.00947} = 1.96$

10. $\sigma_a = \dfrac{1}{1.96} = 0.51 \text{ cm}^2$

$$\sigma_b = \dfrac{1}{1.96 \times 0.746} = 0.685 \text{ cm}^2$$

3–11. ELECTRON THEORY OF THERMOELECTRICITY

To understand why the Seebeck coefficient changes with temperature and carrier density as it does, we shall go one step further in the theory. The essential points are as follows:

Energy Band. As discussed in Sec. 2–18, one of the most important concepts in quantum mechanics is that particles (electrons, protons, etc.)

cannot have just any arbitrary value of energy. There are a certain number of *states* in each energy range ΔE, and each particle must occupy one or the other of the states. The states are quite similar to seats in an opera house. Each seat represents a possible audience, but it may remain unoccupied. Electrons are a type of Fermions characterized by the principle that no two Fermions can occupy the same state.

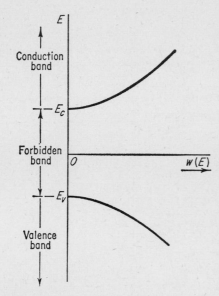

For electrons in solids, the typical density of states $W(E)$ as a function of energy E is shown in Fig. 3–16. For $E_v \leq E \leq E_c$, $W(E) = 0$, which means that it is not possible for an electron in the particular solid to have such an energy value. This is called the *forbidden band*. The energy band below E_v represents electrons tightly bound into the lattice structure of the solid and is called the *valence band*. The energy band above E_c represents free electrons and is called the *conduction band*.

Fig. 3–16. Typical Plots of Density of States versus Energy.

Fermi Factor. The probability of a state's being occupied by an electron depends on E and the temperature, and is given by the *Fermi* factor Eq. (2–89):

$$f(E) = \frac{1}{1 + e^{(E-E_0)/kT}} \tag{3–75}$$

where k is the Boltzmann constant. A plot of $f(E)$ is shown in Fig. 2–9. We note that at absolute zero temperature, $T = 0$, $f(E)$ is 1 for $E < E_0$ and cuts off suddenly at $E = E_0$. The cutoff is more gradual as T is increased.

The energy E_0 is called the *Fermi level*. Its value is determined by the condition of charge balance. The total number of electrons per unit volume must equal the total number of positive charges or protons in all the atomic nuclei per unit volume:

$$\int_0^\infty f(E)W(E)\, dE = N_p \tag{3–76}$$

Equation (3–76) is a rewritten version of Eq. (2–90).

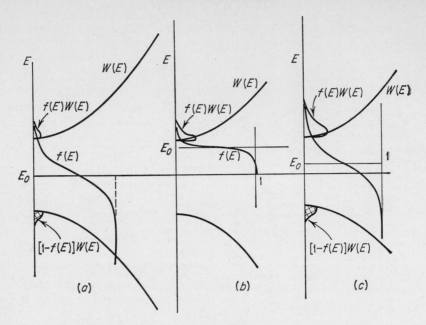

Fig. 3-17. CHANGE IN FERMI-LEVEL WITH TEMPERATURE–A RESULT OF CHARGE BALANCE: (**a**) INTRINSIC SEMICONDUCTOR; (**b**) n-TYPE SEMICONDUCTOR AT ROOM TEMPERATURE; (**c**) SAME n-TYPE SEMICONDUCTOR AT HIGH TEMPERATURE.

Since $f(E)$ is a function of E_0, T, and E, the integral on the left-hand side of Eq. (3–76) is a function of E_0, and T. Equation (3–76) gives E_0 as a function of T. To see this graphically, we plot $w(E)$ and $f(E)$ together in Fig. 3–17. In Fig. 3–17(a), the semiconducting material is not doped, and the total number of electrons is just sufficient to occupy all the states below E_v but nothing above E_c. At non-zero temperature, some of the states above E_c are occupied, as shown by the product $f(E)\,w(E)$, and some of the states below E_v are vacated, as shown by the product $[1 - f(E)]\,W(E)$. To be visible, the products are drawn in an exaggerated scale. The number of electrons above E_c must be equal to the number of states vacated below E_v. Therefore, E_0 is somewhere near the center of the forbidden band. Its exact position is influenced by the fact that $W(E)$ above E_c and $W(E)$ below E_v are not exactly mirror images of each other. The vacated states below E_v become holes. They behave exactly like carriers of positive charges in every way.

In Fig. 3–17(b), the semiconductor is doped with n-type material and there is an excess of electrons. We see that E_0 must be located nearer to

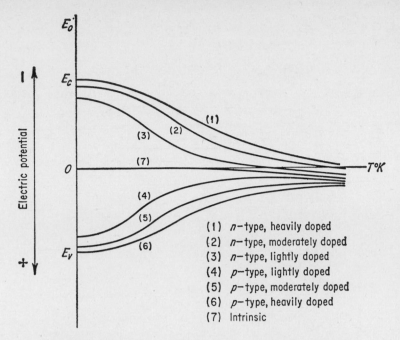

Fig. 3–18. FERMI-LEVEL VERSUS TEMPERATURE FOR SEMICON-DUCTORS WITH DIFFERENT KINDS AND PERCENTAGES OF IMPURITIES.

E_c. In Fig. 3–17(c), we have the same doped semiconductor at a higher temperature. In order to keep the number of electrons unchanged, E_0 must move nearer to the center. A similar situation holds for p-type material except that E_0 is now nearer to E_v. The impurity states are not shown, as they are comparatively very few in number. From the foregoing reasoning, it is not difficult to follow the variations in Fermi-level E_0 with temperature and composition (kind and degree of doping) as shown in Fig. 3–18. Because the number of states above E_c extends to infinity, whereas the number of states below E_v is limited, the E_0 curve of the undoped material bends slightly downward as T is increased. At $T = 0$, E_0 of all the n-type material starts off at some point near E_c. As T is increased, E_0 drifts toward the undoped E_0 curve; and it is slower in drifting the more doped the material is. Similar situation holds for the p-type material.

Seebeck emf. At a p-n junction, in order to have a balance of diffusion flow of electrons, the probability of occupancy of a state by an electron at the same energy level on two sides of the junction must be the same. Consequently, E_0 *is the same on two sides of the junction.*

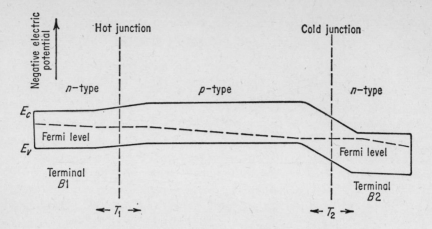

Fig. 3–19. SEEBECK e.m.f. AND THE CHANGE IN FERMI-LEVEL.

Figure 3–19 shows the potential diagram of the thermocouple illustrated in Fig. 3–2, assuming that A is made of p-type material and B is made of n-type material of the same basic semiconductor. In order to examine the Seebeck emf generated, we assume that there is no current flow. The Fermi level is lined up at the junctions. As there is a larger potential difference at the cold junction than at the hot junction, B_2 is at a higher positive potential than B_1. The open circuit Seebeck emf is seen to be

$$e_{pn}(T_1, T_2) = E_{0p}(T_2) - E_{0n}(T_2) - [E_{0p}(T_1) - E_{0n}(T_1)] \qquad (3\text{--}77)$$

In Eq. (3–77), E_{0p} and E_{0n} are the Fermi levels in terms of electrical potential rather than energy. The potential variations in the elements themselves are neglected. Inside the same material, the density of charge carriers does not change much from section to section. As there is to be no current flow, the potential E_c and E_v must not vary much.

Differentiating Eq. (3–77) with respect to T_1 gives

$$\frac{\partial e_{pn}(T_1, T_2)}{\partial T_1} = -\frac{dE_{0p}(T_1)}{dT_1} + \frac{dE_{0n}(T_1)}{dT_1} \qquad (3\text{--}78)$$

Comparing Eq. (3–14b) and Eq. (3–78) gives the Seebeck coefficient as

$$S_{pn}(T_1) = -\frac{dE_{0p}(T_1)}{dT_1} + \frac{dE_{0n}(T_1)}{dT_1} \qquad (3\text{--}79)$$

Comparing Eq. (3–79) and Eq. (3–25) gives

$$S_{\mathrm{p}}(T) = -\frac{dE_{0\mathrm{p}}(T)}{dT}$$

$$S_{\mathrm{n}}(T) = -\frac{dE_{0\mathrm{n}}(T)}{dT} \tag{3–80}$$

Seebeck coefficient. Equation (3–80) gives a qualitative explanation of Fig. 3–9. We note that, in terms of positive electric potential instead of electronic energy, Fig. 3–18 is upside down, which cancels out the sign in Eq. (3–80). For a p-type material, E_0 is a rising curve. Its derivative dE_0/dT is positive and the Seebeck coefficient is also positive. For a lightly doped material, E_0 rises quickly and also saturates quickly. Consequently, dE_0/dT has a higher peak value and also drops off at a much lower temperature. The Seebeck coefficient for n-type material can be explained in much the same way, except that, owing to the downward trend of the neutral E_0 curve, the Seebeck coefficient of the n-type material is sustained over a larger temperature range. Thus we have explained all the three items of experimental observations on the Seebeck coefficient in Sec. 3–8.

Peltier Effect. When a current is passed from the p side to the n side, electrons pass from the n side to the p side, and holes pass from the p side to the n side. Once the electrons get to the p side, they are likely to drop into a hole (or rather fill a vacancy in the valence band) since there are so many holes available. When an electron drops into a hole, both the hole and the electron disappear and energy is released. Similarly, once a hole gets into the n side, it combines with one of the electrons and energy is released. Therefore, passing positive current from p side to n side results in a release of thermal energy from the junction to its surroundings (or to the reservoir). If a positive current is passed from the n side to the p side, holes must go from the n side to the p side and electrons must go from the p side to the n side. On the n side, electrons must jump from the valence band into the conduction band in order to create new holes to replace the ones which have left. Similarly, more electrons have to jump from the valence band into the conduction band on the p side to replace the electrons which have left. In order for the electrons to do this, energy must be supplied from the environment. Therefore, in passing a positive current from n side to p side, energy is absorbed.

Seebeck Effect in Metals. The large variation of Fermi level in a semiconductor with temperature is due to the presence of a large energy gap. By contrast, in a good conductive metal, the Fermi level falls right into a dense crowd of energy states and it does not change much with temperature. As this effect is now hundreds of times smaller, it becomes of comparable magnitude with another effect, the electric potential or work function. The electron theory of thermoelectricity for metals is therefore more involved. As the effect is small, however, and not likely to be very useful, we shall not go into it.

REFERENCES

1. Cadoff, I. B., and E. Miller, *Thermoelectric Materials and Devices*. New York: Reinhold Publishing Co., 1960.

2. Kaye, J., and J. A. Welsh, *Direct Conversion of Heat to Electricity*, chap. 14–21. New York: John Wiley & Sons, 1959.

3. Sproull, R. L., *Modern Physics*, pp. 220–363. New York: John Wiley & Sons, 1956.

PROBLEMS

3–1. The thermoelectric power of a certain material A is given as

$$S_a(T) = (200 + T)(400 - T) \times 10^{-7} \text{ volt/deg C}$$

where T is in degrees C. Calculate its Peltier and Thomson coefficients as a function of T.

3–2. A certain material B has $S_b(T) = -S_a(T)$, and $S_a(T)$ is the same as that of Prob. 3–1. The materials are made into a refrigeration engine operating between temperatures $-30°C$ and $30°C$. Draw a diagram showing the direction of electric current and the directions of heat transfer due to thermoelectric effects. Calculate the amount of heat absorbed and generated at the junctions and in the elements owing to the passage of 10 amp of current for an hour.

3–3. If the external source of emf is replaced by a load and the refrigeration chamber is used as a fuel chamber, will the direction of current be reversed? Why?

3–4. A 100-kw, 115-volt thermoelectric generator is to be designed to operate between an input temperature of $1500°K$ and an ambient temperature of $1000°K$. The following properties of material are given:

$$S_{ab} \text{ at } 1250°K = 0.0012 \text{ volt/}°K$$

$$K_a = 0.02 \text{ watt/cm-}°K$$

$$\rho_a = 0.01 \text{ ohm-cm}$$

$$K_b = 0.03 \text{ watt/cm-}°K$$

$$\rho_b = 0.012 \text{ ohm-cm}$$

The current density in the thermoelectric elements is limited to 20 amp/cm^2, and the design is aimed at maximum thermal efficiency. Calculate

1. The maximum thermal efficiency
2. The number of thermal couples in series
3. The sizes of the thermal elements
4. The open circuit voltage
5. Input and rejected heat at
   (a) Full load condition
   (b) No load condition

3–5. A steam turbine and generator unit operating at an input temperature of 1000°K and an ambient temperature of 350°K has a thermal efficiency of 30% and a generator efficiency of 92%. What is the over-all efficiency? If the turbogenerator is used to utilize the heat rejected in Prob. 3–4, what is the over-all efficiency of the combined unit?

3–6. Assume that the Seebeck coefficient S_{ab} is 0.002 volt/°K in the temperature range from $-50°$ to $+50°$C, and the other properties are as given in Prob. 3–4. Design a single-stage thermoelectric refrigerator which has a cooling capacity of 500 Btu per hour at a temperature of $-20°$C. The ambient temperature is 25°C. Allow 10°C difference between the hot junction and ambient and between the cold junction and cooling load. The electric source has 6 volts. The design is for maximum coefficient of performance. Calculate

1. Coefficient of performance
2. The number of thermal couples in series
3. The sizes of thermal elements
4. The current required to keep the cooling load at $-20°$C. (That is, the thermoelectric cooling is just sufficient to balance its own conduction and i^2R loss.)

3–7. Show that, for a refrigeration engine or heat pump,

$$\left(\frac{Q_2}{Q_1}\right)_{\max} = \frac{T_2 M_0 - T_1}{T_1 M_0 - T_2}$$

3–8. Show that, for a two-stage refrigeration engine operating between temperatures T_1, T_2, and T_2, T_3 respectively, the optimum over-all thermal exchange ratio is

$$\frac{Q_3}{Q_1} = \left(\frac{T_2 M_0 - T_1}{T_1 M_0 - T_2}\right)\left(\frac{T_3 M_0' - T_2}{T_2 M_0' - T_3}\right)$$

Assume that M_0 remains the same for the two stages and T_2 can be freely chosen. Show that

$$\left(\frac{Q_3}{Q_1}\right)_{\max} = \left(\frac{r M_0 - 1}{r - M_0}\right)^2$$

where $r = \sqrt{T_3/T_1}$.

3–9. Could the result of Prob. 3–8 be generalized to n stages? If so, show how.

3–10. A refrigeration machine is designed for 500 Btu per hour at $-100°C$. The ambient temperature is 25°C. The best available material has a figure of merit $T_m z = 3$. Calculate the least input power required if the refrigeration engine is to be one-stage, two-stage, or three-stage?

3–11. A thermoelectric heat pump is used to extract heat from 0°F weather to heat a home at 70°F, and the figure of merit of available material is assumed to be $T_m z = 2.5$. What is the maximum percentage savings in electric power consumed compared to direct electric heating?

CHAPTER FOUR

THERMIONIC CONVERTERS

The thermionic effect was first discovered by Thomas Edison about 1880. Though its significance escaped even Edison at the time, it was one of the fundamental discoveries which made radio engineering what it is today. The thermionic effect has been given serious consideration as a means for converting thermal energy into electrical energy only during the past few years. Two essential difficulties are in the way of making thermionic converters efficient: the space-charge effect and the radiation of heat. Today, these difficulties are only partially overcome.

This chapter gives an analysis of the scientific effects involved and also presents equations for designing and predicting the performance of thermionic converters.

4-1. GENERAL DESCRIPTION

Thermionic emission can be utilized to convert heat into electricity. The basic elements of such a device are illustrated in Fig. 4–1. A hot cathode emits electrons which travel across a narrow gap to a relatively cool anode. If the cathode and anode are connected externally, the electrons collected on the anode return to the cathode through the external circuit. Thus an electric current i is established, as shown in Fig. 4–1. If a load is inserted in the external circuit, a potential difference is developed across it with the signs as indicated. Insofar as the external circuit is concerned, the cathode is the positive terminal and the anode is the negative terminal of the thermionic generator.

The potential V tends to retard the flight of electrons from cathode to anode. The electrons emitted from the cathode have various initial velocities in the direction x of the anode. Let v_x denote this component of velocity. When V is increased, it takes electrons with larger v_x to reach the anode. As fewer of the emitted electrons possess the required v_x, i is decreased with increased V. Thus, the voltage output of the generator is limited by the initial velocities of the electrons.

On the thermal side, heat is supplied to the cathode to compensate for the energy taken by the emitted electrons and for loss of heat from the cathode due to radiation, convection, and conduction. Generally, the diode is of parallel plate construction, as indicated in Fig. 4–1. As the external surface of the cathode is entirely used for transfer of heat Q_1 from the heat source to the cathode, the afore-mentioned loss of heat from the cathode is mostly transferred to the anode. It must be removed in order to keep the anode temperature from rising too high. With a high anode temperature, the anode also emits electrons toward the cathode and the net current i is reduced.

From the preceding description, we see that a thermionic engine follows exactly the general format of a heat engine: Thermal energy is applied to it at a high temperature; part of this energy is converted to work (electrical energy), and the other part is transferred away at a lower temperature.

4-2. A REVIEW OF THERMIONIC EMISSION

In order to predict the performance of a thermionic engine, it is necessary to have some familiarity with the basic facts about thermionic emission, which are summarized in this section.

4-2a. WORK FUNCTION

Electrons move freely inside a metal but rarely escape from its surface. One may wonder what is the nature of the force that keeps the electrons from escaping.

The answer is readily found in the familiar image force of electrostatics. Referring to Fig. 4–2, as soon as an electron with charge $-e$ has escaped from the metal surface, positive charges are induced on the latter. The total effect of the induced charges is the same as that of a positive charge

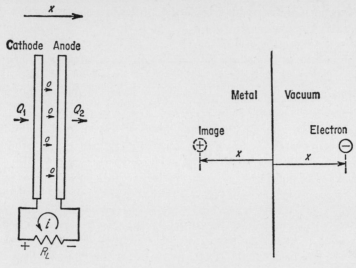

Fig. 4–1. A Thermionic Converter of Heat to Electrical Energy.

Fig. 4–2. Image Potential–the Origin of Work Function.

e at the same distance x inside the metal surface. Consequently there is a force F pulling the electron back to the metal:

$$F = \frac{e^2}{16\pi\epsilon_0 x^2} \qquad (4\text{–}1)$$

Since the approximation of the metal surface by a smooth plane breaks down when the electron is too close to the metal surface, Eq. (4–1) is not expected to hold for values of x less than the spacing of the atoms.

The equivalent potential of the work required to pull an electron free from a metal surface is called the *work function*, and is denoted by Φ. To check the validity of our explanation, let us assume the following crude model of image force:

$$F = 0, \qquad \text{if } x < x_1$$

$$= \frac{e^2}{16\pi\epsilon_0 x^2}, \qquad \text{if } x \geq x_1 \qquad (4\text{–}2)$$

Then

$$e\Phi = \int_{x_1}^{\infty} \frac{e^2}{16\pi\epsilon_0 x^2}\, dx = \frac{e^2}{16\pi\epsilon_0 x_1}$$

$$\Phi = \frac{e}{16\pi\epsilon_0 x_1} \qquad (4\text{–}3)$$

The work function for tungsten is 4.52 volts, which corresponds to a value of x_1:

$$x_1 = \frac{e}{16\pi\epsilon_0\Phi} = \frac{1.021 \times 10^{-19}}{16\pi \times 1/36\pi \times 10^{-9} \times 4.52} = 0.79 \times 10^{-10} \text{ meter}$$

It is of the order of magnitude of the distance between two atoms.

From a phenomenological point of view, we may regard the work function Φ as a drop in electric potential at a point "outside" a metal surface relative to a point inside the metal surface. There is no need to specify how far outside. The smallest distance of practical interest is of the order of 10^{-6} m. Even at this close proximity, the change of electrical potential due to image force is only 3.6×10^{-4} volt which is quite negligible in comparison to the usual experimental error of about 0.01 volt in measured work function. Thus one may represent the work function as a step change in potential at the metal surface.

4-2b. ENERGY DISTRIBUTION OF ELECTRONS INSIDE METAL

In electrostatics, we like to say that the potential at a certain conductor is φ. What we mean is the following: (1) A charge e on the conductor possesses an energy $e\varphi$. (2) If a conductor of higher potential is in contact with a conductor of lower potential, positive charge will flow from the former to the latter until the two potentials are equalized.

With our present-day knowledge of conductors, semiconductors, etc., the foregoing simple picture must be modified. The electrons occupying any minute part of a conductor are distributed over a wide range of energy levels. Thus the concept of "energy possessed by an electric charge" becomes vague. The potential at a conductor, however, can still be precisely defined as its Fermi level in the sense of Statement 2. If two conductors of equal Fermi level are brought into contact, the net exchange of charge between the two conductors is zero.

As discussed in Sec. 3–11, there are infinite number of states in a solid for electrons to occupy. Each state has its assigned energy. The states are crowded into allowed energy bands (valence band, conduction band, etc.) with wide gaps or forbidden bands in between. A metal differs from an insulator or a semiconductor in that its Fermi level falls in an allowed band rather than in a forbidden band.

Since there are infinitely more states than the number of electrons available to occupy them, only the lower energy states are filled or nearly filled. The higher energy states are rarely occupied. The probability that a state of energy E is occupied is given by the Fermi factor of Eq. (2–89).

If $E - E_0 \gg kT$, Eq. (2-89) becomes

$$f(E) = e^{-(E-E_0)/kT} \tag{4-4}$$

Equation (4–4) shows that the states with $E - E_0 \gg kT$ are rarely occupied, and the probability of their occupation decreases exponentially with increasing E.

4-2c. RICHARDSON'S EQUATION

If an electron arrives at the metal surface with a normal velocity v_n (the velocity component in the direction of the normal) satisfying

$$v_n > \sqrt{\frac{2e\Phi}{m}} \tag{4-5}$$

it escapes from the metal or is "emitted." If Eq. (4–5) is not satisfied, the electron is pulled back by image force into the metal.

By calculating the number of electrons arriving at the surface with sufficient v_n, the thermionic current density is shown to be

$$J_0 = A T^2 e^{-e\Phi/kT} \tag{4-6}$$

Equation (4–6) is known as the *Richardson-Dushman equation*. Theoretically, A is a universal constant 1.20×10^6 amp/m². The measured values of A and Φ are given in Table 4–1. The discrepancy between the experi-

TABLE 4-1

THERMIONIC EMISSION CONSTANTS

Metal	Φ (in volts)	A (in amp/m²; very approximate)
Cr	4.60	0.48×10^6
Cs	1.81	...
K	1.9–2.46	...
Mo	4.20	0.55
Na	2.5	...
Ni	4.61	0.30
Pt	5.32	0.32
Ta	4.19	0.55
W	4.52	0.60
Th − W	2.63	0.03
BaO + SrO (Oxides)	1.03	10^{-4}

mental and theoretical values of A is owing to the way A is determined experimentally. The work function is *assumed* to be independent of temperature, and the surface of the cathode is *assumed* to be homogeneous. As a matter of fact, we know that the surface cannot be homogeneous, because of the crystalline structure of metal, and that the work function Φ generally increases with T. As the formula fitting is done on the erroneous assumptions cited, the errors are absorbed in measured value of A. For instance:

$$\Phi = \Phi_0 + \Phi_1 T + \cdots$$

Then,

$$J_0 = A T^2 e^{-e\Phi_0/kT} e^{-e\Phi_1/k}$$

The entire constant factor is the measured value of A:

$$A_{\text{meas}} = A e^{-e\Phi_1/k} \tag{4-7}$$

Although the experimental evidence of Table 4–1 appears to contradict the theoretical result that A is a universal constant, it is explainable in terms of Eq. (4–7). On the other hand, if A were different for two different metals, we should be able to break the second law of thermodynamics, as we shall see shortly.

4-2d. ENERGY DISTRIBUTION OF EMITTED ELECTRONS

The forward velocities of emitted electrons are distributed over a wide range. Let E_x denote the forward kinetic energy in electron-volts

$$E_x \equiv \frac{m}{2e} v_x^2 \tag{4-8}$$

The fraction of J having forward kinetic energy in the range E_x to $E_x + dE_x$ is obtained from Eq. (4–4) as

$$dJ = \frac{J_0 e}{kT} e^{-eE_x/kT} dE_x \tag{4-9}$$

Example 4–1: What value of Φ_1 would account for the difference between the experimental value of $A = 0.60 \times 10^6$ for tungsten and the theoretical value of 1.20×10^6?

SOLUTION: Equation (4–7) can be written as

$$\Phi_1 = \frac{k}{e} \log \frac{A}{A_{\text{meas}}} = 8.616 \times 10^{-5} \times 0.693$$

$$= 5.97 \times 10^{-5} \text{ ev/}^\circ\text{K}$$

The answer shows that the change in work function is slightly over 1% for a temperature change of 1000°K.

Example 4-2: At a cathode temperature of 2200°K, what fraction of emitted electrons has a forward kinetic energy of 1 ev or more?

SOLUTION: Integrating Eq. (4–9) gives

$$J_{E_x \geq V} = \int_V^\infty \frac{J_0 e}{kT}\, e^{-eE_x/kT}\, dE_x = J_0 e^{-eV/kT}$$

Let $V = 1$ volt. Then,

$$\frac{J_{E_x \geq V}}{J_0} = e^{-11,600/2,200} = e^{-5.27} = 0.00517$$

Only slightly over $\frac{1}{2}\%$ of the electrons has a forward kinetic energy of 1 volt or more.

4-3. ANALYSIS OF A HIGH-VACUUM THERMIONIC CONVERTER

We shall assume that the simple thermionic diode of Fig. 4–1 is placed in a container of high vacuum. The space between the anode and cathode is occupied only by electrons in transit. We shall analyze its performance in the following order: potential distribution; net current; power and efficiency.

4-3a. POTENTIAL DISTRIBUTION

The electric potential distribution of the thermionic diode is illustrated in Fig. 4–3. There is a potential difference V_0 between the Fermi levels of the cathode and anode owing to voltage drop V across the load, Seebeck effect of the external conductor, and iR drop in the external conductor:

$$V_0 = V + iR - S(T_1 - T_2) \tag{4-10}$$

where S = Seebeck coefficient of external conductor,

　　T_1 = cathode temperature,

　　T_2 = anode temperature.

If the external conductor is p type or thermoelectrically positive, its Seebeck emf tends to cause a positive current to flow into the anode at the cold junction. Therefore the thermionic potential is reinforced by the Seebeck emf, as is expressed in Eq. (4–10).

At the surfaces of the electrodes, the electric potentials drop by Φ_c and Φ_a respectively, where Φ_c is the work function of the cathode, and Φ_a is the work function of the anode. Because of space-charge effect, the electric potential φ between the two electrodes is not a linear function of x but concaves downward, as is shown in Fig. 4-3. The space-charge effect increases the maximum negative potential between the electrodes from $-(V_0 + \Phi_a)$ to $-E_p$. It reduces the thermionic current by repelling all electrons which have a forward kinetic energy less than $e(E_p - \Phi_c)$.

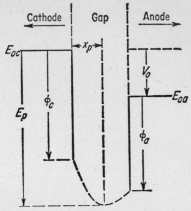

Fig. 4-3. ELECTRIC POTENTIAL DISTRIBUTION INSIDE A THERMIONIC CONVERTER.

Obviously, E_p increases with the spacing between the two electrodes. In order to reduce E_p to tolerable value, it is found that the spacing should be of the order of 10^{-4} in. Although experimental thermionic diodes have been made with such close spacing, it is by no means an easy thing to do. It constitutes a serious limitation in the usefulness of high-vacuum diodes.

4-3b. THERMIONIC CURRENT, $T_1 \gg T_2$

To begin with, let us assume the anode to be sufficiently cold so that the thermionic current emitted from it is negligible. Among the electrons emitted from the cathode, only those with a forward kinetic energy E_x equal to $E_p - \Phi_c$ or larger succeed in reaching the anode. The less energetic ones are repulsed back to the cathode by the space-charge potential and do not contribute to the net flow of current. Referring to Eq. (4-9), the net electron current density from cathode to anode is given by

$$J_1 = \int_{E_p - \Phi_c}^{\infty} \frac{J_0 e}{kT_1} e^{-eE_x/kT_1} \, dE_x$$

$$= J_0 \, e^{e(E_p - \Phi_c)/kT_1}$$

As
$$J_0 = A T_1^2 e^{-e\Phi_c/kT_1}$$

the above equation becomes

$$J_1 = A T_1^2 e^{-eE_p/kT_1} \tag{4-11}$$

An interesting point about Eq. (4-11) is that J_1 *is independent of the cathode work function* Φ_c.

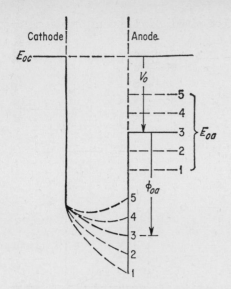

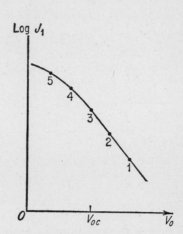

Fig. 4–4. Electric Potential Distributions for Different Output Voltages V_0

Fig. 4–5. Current Density as a Function of Output Voltage.

Now let us investigate the variation of J_1 as V_0 is varied. Figure 4–4 illustrates the change in potential distribution between the electrodes. The five levels of V_0 are in one-to-one correspondence with the five end points of the potential distribution curves. At the level marked 3, $d\varphi/dx = 0$ at the anode surface, and the peak negative potential $-E_p$ coincides with the anode potential $-(V_0 + \Phi_{0a})$. This value of V_0 is called the *critical voltage* and is denoted as V_{0c}. For $V_0 > V_{0c}$, (curves 1 and 2) the lowest electric potential is $-(V_0 + \Phi_{0a})$. For $V_0 < V_{0c}$ (curves 4 and 5), the potential minimum $-E_p$ occurs somewhere between the two electrodes. Figure 4–5 illustrates the change in current density with V_0. We recall Eq. (4–11) which shows that $\log J_1$ varies linearly as E_p. For $V_0 > V_{0c}$, $E_p = V_0 + \Phi_{0a}$, and $\log J_1$ decreases linearly. For $V_0 < V_{0c}$, while E_p decreases as V_0 is decreased, E_p does not change as much as V_0. Consequently, $\log J_1$ also tends to level off. The point of maximum output occurs at a value of V_0 somewhat below V_{0c}, for instance, level 4 in Fig. 4–4.

Another aspect is the variation of J_1 with the spacing between electrodes. A universal equation gives this relation as [4]

$$J_1 = 9.664 \times 10^{-6} \frac{V_T^{3/2}}{x_p^2} \text{ amp/m}^2 \tag{4–12}$$

where x_p is the distance from the cathode to the potential minimum in meters, and V_T is the voltage equivalent of cathode temperature:

$$V_T = \frac{kT_1}{e} \qquad (4\text{–}13)$$

In deriving Eq. (4–12), it is assumed that $E_p - \Phi_c$ is at least four or five times larger than V_T. The remarkable point about Eq. (4–12) is its entire independence of E_p and Φ_c. Physically, this is fairly easy to see. Given V_T and J_1, E_p is implicitly given because of Eq. (4–11). Figure 4–6 illustrates the variation of φ about the potential minimum point. The curve is not symmetrical because the electron density is far greater on the cathode side. Given any Φ_c, a point P is located on the φ curve and x_d is determined as the horizontal distance from P to the potential minimum. As the electron density increases exponentially with $-x$, the φ curve bends upward sharply to an almost vertical attitude. The change in x_d is negligible for a substantial change in φ from $-\Phi_{c1}$ to $-\Phi_{c2}$.

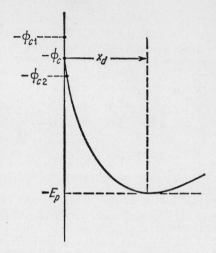

Fig. 4–6. Typical Electric Potential Distribution Illustrating the Insensitivity of x_0 to Cathode Potential.

Although x_d is not the full separation between the two electrodes except for $V_0 = V_{0c}$, it nevertheless gives an indication of the latter. The need for close spacing is illustrated in the following example:

Example 4–3: A thermionic diode is to be designed for a current density of 1 amp/cm² at the critical point, $V_0 = V_{0c}$. The operating temperature is 2500°K. Calculate E_p and the spacing between electrodes.

Solution: Equation (4–11) gives E_p as

$$E_p = \frac{kT_1}{e} \log \frac{AT_1^2}{J_1}$$

$$= 8.616 \times 10^{-5} \times 2500 \log \frac{1.2 \times 10^6 \times 2500^2}{10^4}$$

$$= 0.2154 \log 750 \times 10^6 = 0.2154 \times 20.4$$

$$= 4.32 \text{ volts}$$

Equation (4–12) gives

$$x_p^2 = 9.664 \times 10^{-6} \times \frac{0.2154^{3/2}}{10^4} = 9.664 \times 10^{-11}$$

$$x_p = 9.83 \times 10^{-6} \text{ m}$$

4-3c. THERMIONIC CURRENT, $T_1 \cong T_2$

When T_2 is sufficiently high, the thermionic current emitted by the anode is no longer negligible. The net current density becomes

$$J_n = J_1 - J_2$$
$$= A_1 T_1^2 e^{-eE_p/kT_1} - A_2 T_2^2 e^{-e(E_p-V_0)/kT_2} \qquad (4\text{–}14)$$

Thus the thermionic current density is lowered by the second term. Another effect implicit in Eq. (4–14), but nevertheless just as important, is the increase in magnitude of E_p due to increased charge density. A larger E_p further reduces the current in either direction.

Equation (4–14) also shows why A is a universal constant. If $A_1 \neq A_2$ and $V_0 = 0$, J_n does not vanish at $T_1 = T_2$. It is a routine matter to show that with some slight V_0, electric power is delivered to the external load. Thus heat from a single reservoir with $T = T_1 = T_2$ is converted into electric energy, a result which contradicts the second law of thermodynamics.

Therefore, in calculating J_n for very small temperature difference $T_1 - T_2$, we use a single constant A for A_1 and A_2 in Eq. (4–14). T_2 can be expressed as

$$T_2 = T_1 - \Delta T$$

and V_0 itself can be regarded as a small variation. Let

$$f(T, V) \equiv A T^2 e^{-eV/kT} \qquad (4\text{–}15)$$

Then

$$J_n = f(T_1, E_p) - f(T_1 - \Delta T, E_p - V_0)$$
$$\cong f_T(T_1, E_p)\,\Delta T + f_V(T_1, E_p)V_0 \qquad (4\text{–}16)$$

where f_T and f_V are partial derivatives of f with respect to T and V. These derivatives can be readily evaluated as follows:

$$\log f(T, V) = \log A + 2 \log T - \frac{eV}{kT}$$

$$\frac{\Delta f}{f} = \frac{2\,\Delta T}{T} + \frac{eV}{kT}\frac{\Delta T}{T} - \frac{e\,\Delta V}{kT} \qquad (4\text{–}17)$$

Let V_T denote kT_1/e. Since J_1 is equal to $f(T_1, E_p)$, Eq. (4–17) gives

$$f_T(T_1, E_p) = \left(2 + \frac{E_p}{V_T}\right)\frac{J_1}{T_1}$$

$$f_V(T_1, E_p) = -\frac{J_1}{V_T}$$

Substituting the preceding expressions into Eq. (4–16) and rearranging terms, we obtain finally

$$V_0 = (2V_T + E_p)\frac{\Delta T}{T_1} - \frac{V_T}{J_1} \cdot J_n \tag{4–18}$$

Equation (4–18) illustrates the similarity between a thermionic diode and a source of emf with an internal impedance.

4-3d. LOSS AND EFFICIENCY

The thermal input into the cathode consists of two essential components:

1. Energy carried away per second by emitted electrons, q_e
2. Energy lost per second due to radiation, q_r

We shall evaluate q_e first. If an electron is emitted and later repelled back to the cathode, it brings back as much energy as what it has left with, and no change of energy takes place. Only electrons which succeeded in reaching the anode are energy conveyers. The average forward kinetic energy carried away by each electron is

$$e\overline{E_x} = \frac{\displaystyle\int_{E_p}^{\infty} eE_x e^{-eE_x/kT_1}\, dE_x}{\displaystyle\int_{E_p}^{\infty} e^{-eE_x/kT_1}\, dE_x}$$

$$= kT_1\left(\frac{eE_p}{kT_1} + 1\right) = eE_p + kT_1 \tag{4–19}$$

Since the average kinetic energies in the y and z directions are $kT_1/2$ each, the average energy carried away by each electron is $eE_p + 2kT_1$. Similarly, the average energy carried to the cathode by an electron emitted from the anode is $eE_p + 2kT_2$. Therefore,

$$q_e = \frac{J_1}{e}(eE_p + 2kT_1) + \frac{J_2}{e}(eE_p + 2kT_2)$$

$$= J_nE_p + \frac{2k}{e}(J_1T_1 - J_2T_2) \tag{4-20}$$

The energy lost per second due to radiation is

$$q_r = \nu F(T_1^4 - T_2^4) \tag{4-21}$$

where F is the Stefan-Boltzmann constant 5.67×10^{-8} watt/m^2($^\circ$K)^4, and ν is a constant less than unity. Its value depends on the absorption coefficients of the surfaces of the two electrodes.

Including the external circuit, the total output, input, and efficiency are given as:

$$W = iV = i(V_0 + S(T_1 - T_2) - iR] \tag{4-22}$$

$$q_1 = ST_1 + K(T_1 - T_2) + q_e + q_r \tag{4-23}$$

$$\eta_{th} = \frac{W}{q_1} \tag{4-24}$$

where S, R, and K, are the thermoelectric power, electrical resistance, and thermal conductance of the external conductor.

4-3e. FIGURE OF MERIT

When $T_1 - T_2$ is small,

$$q_e = J_nE_p + \frac{2k}{e}(J_1 - J_2)T_1 + \frac{2k}{e}J_1(T_1 - T_2)$$

$$= J_n(E_p + 2V_T) + 2V_TJ_1\frac{\Delta T}{T} \tag{4-25}$$

$$q_r = 4\nu FT_1^3 \Delta T \tag{4-26}$$

The total input to the thermionic diode itself is

$$q_e + q_r = J_n(E_p + 2V_T) + \left(4\nu FT_1^3 + \frac{2V_TJ_1}{T_1}\right)\Delta T \tag{4-27}$$

Equations (4–18) and (4–27) illustrate the close resemblance between a thermionic diode and a thermoelectric element. In fact, we can consider a thermionic diode as a thermoelectric element with the following parameters:

$$S = -\frac{1}{T_1}(E_p + 2V_T) \tag{4-28a}$$

$$R = \frac{V_T}{J_1\sigma_e} \tag{4-28b}$$

$$K = \left(4\nu FT_1^3 + \frac{2V_TJ_1}{T_1}\right)\sigma_e \tag{4-28c}$$

where σ_e is the emission area. The figure of merit $\theta = TS^2/RK$ can be calculated as a function of cathode temperature. Assuming negligible space charge effect, E_p is simply the anode work function, and θ can be written as

$$\theta = \frac{[(\Phi/V_T) + 2]^2}{[(4\nu FT_1^4)/V_TJ_1] + 2} \tag{4-29}$$

Equation (4–29) can be simplified as follows:

$$\frac{\nu FT_1^4}{V_TJ_1} = \frac{\nu FT_1^4}{V_TAT_1^2e^{-\Phi/V_T}}$$

$$= \frac{F}{A_0}\left(\frac{e}{k}\right)^2 \cdot \left(\frac{\nu\Phi A_0}{A}\right) \cdot \left(\frac{V_T}{\Phi}\right)e^{\Phi/V_T}$$

$$= 6.36 \times 10^{-6}\rho\left(\frac{V_T}{\Phi}\right)e^{\Phi/V_T} \tag{4-30}$$

where $\rho = \nu\Phi A_0/A$ is a constant of the metal. Combining Eq. (4–29) and Eq. (4–30), we note that θ is a function of V_T/Φ with ρ as parameter. The calculated result is plotted in Fig. 4–7.

Example 4–4: A high-vacuum thermionic diode is made of tungsten electrodes. The areas of the electrodes are 4 cm² each and the spacing between the electrode is sufficiently small so that space-charge effect can be neglected. Calculate the open-circuit voltage V_{0c} and internal impedance R_i at a cathode temperature of 2500°K and anode temperature of 2400°K.

SOLUTION: Neglecting space-charge effect,

$$E_p = \Phi = 4.52 \text{ volts}$$

$$V_T = \frac{2500°K}{11600°K/\text{volt}} = 0.215 \text{ volt}$$

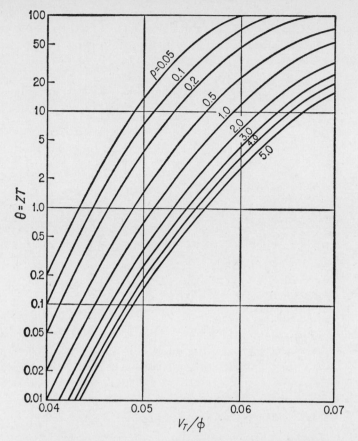

Fig. 4-7. THE EQUIVALENT FIGURE OF MERIT $\theta = S^2 T / KR$ OF A THERMIONIC CONVERTER VERSUS V_T/Φ, WITH $\rho = \nu \Phi A_0 / A$ AS PARAMETER.

From Eq. (4-18), an *approximate* calculation can be made:

$$V_{0c} = (2V_T + E_p) \frac{\Delta T}{T_1} = (0.215 \times 2 + 4.52) \times \frac{100}{2500}$$

$$= 0.198 \text{ volt}$$

$$J_1 = 0.60 \times 10^6 \times 2500^2 \, e^{-4.52/0.215}$$

$$= 3.75 \times 10^{12} \times 10^{-0.434 \times 4.52/0.215}$$

$$= 3.75 \times 10^{12} \times 10^{-9.12} = 2840 \text{ amp/m}^2$$

$$R_i = \frac{V_T}{J_1 \sigma} = \frac{0.215}{2840 \times 4 \times 10^{-4}} = 0.189 \text{ ohm}$$

Example 4–5: For the diode of Prob. 4–4, assume $\nu = 0.01$ and calculate its figure of merit.

SOLUTION: From Eq. (4–28), Eq. (4–29), and Eq. (4–30)

$$S = -\frac{1}{2500}(0.215 \times 2 + 4.52) = 0.00198$$

$$R = 0.189 \text{ ohm}$$

$$K = \left(4 \times 0.01 \times 5.67 \times 10^{-8} \times 2500^3 + \frac{2 \times 0.215 \times 2840}{2500}\right) \times 4 \times 10^{-4}$$

$$= (35.4 + 0.49) \times 4 \times 10^{-4} = 0.0144 \text{ watt/}^\circ K$$

$$\theta = \frac{2500 \times (1.98 \times 10^{-3})^2}{0.189 \times 0.0144} = 3.6$$

4-4. THE GASEOUS DIODES

From the discussion of Sec. 4–3, we see that, although the performance of thermionic diodes is promising, it is quite difficult to achieve the required close spacing of the electrodes to realize such good performance or even tolerable performance. One way out of this difficulty is to use ionized vapor to neutralize the space charge, and the gaseous thermionic diode is obtained. We shall study the gaseous diode in the following order:

1. Supply and ionization of gaseous atoms
2. Control of the density of ions
3. Voltage, current characteristics
4. Input, efficiency

4-4a. SUPPLY AND IONIZATION OF THE GASEOUS ATOMS

Just like thyratrons, the gaseous thermionic diodes derive their ionized molecules or atoms from metallic vapor. Cesium is most frequently used because it has relatively low ionization energy as well as work function. The advantage of a low work function can be explained as follows: Because of the low temperature of the anode, a thin layer of the vaporized metal is deposited on the anode surface. As the work function is a surface effect, the anode work function Φ_a is that of the deposit rather than that of the host metal.

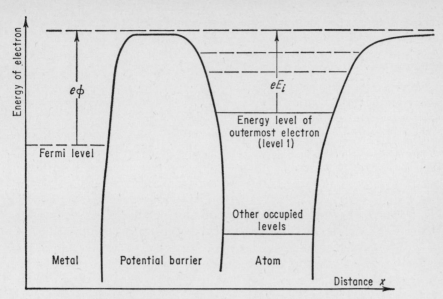

Fig. 4–8. Potential Energy Distribution and Energy Levels of an Atom in Contact with the Cathode.

The ionization can be accomplished in three ways:

1. Ionization by thermal agitation in an externally heated arc
2. Ionization by auxiliary discharge, in other words, by collision with electrons which have been accelerated electrically to a sufficiently high speed
3. Ionization by resonance

For the present application, the third method is by far the simplest and the most efficient. We shall explain its mechanism presently. The electronic energy levels of an atom in contact with a metallic surface is illustrated in Fig. 4–8. In terms of electric potential, the diagram is upside down, in the sense that the electric potential is increasingly negative in the upward direction. At the energy range we are considering, the electronic energy levels inside the metal are so closely packed that they can be considered continuous. These energy levels are not shown explicitly. The energy levels above the Fermi level are nearly empty whereas the ones below are nearly full. Even in seeming "contact," the atom is still at some atomic lengths away from the metal surface, and the "image force" we discussed in Sec. 4–2 gives rise to a potential barrier between the metallic electrons and electrons of the atom. The atomic energy levels are discrete. Those occupied by electrons are shown in solid horizontal lines; the unoccupied ones are shown in broken lines. The top reference line corresponds to the energy of an electron at infinity. E_i is the ionization potential of the atom, and Φ is the work function of the metal. The first occupied energy level of the atom is at an energy eE_i below the reference line, and will be referred to as energy level (1).

If $\Phi > E_i$, energy level (1) is above the Fermi level, and there are many unoccupied metallic energy levels of about the same energy. In classical mechanics, an electron at energy level (1) cannot possibly penetrate the potential barrier and arrive inside the metal. In quantum mechanics, however, a large potential barrier means simply a small coefficient of coupling, and the energy levels at two sides of the barrier are similar to high Q resonant circuits. If the natural frequencies of two resonant circuits are the same, a signal can be transferred almost fully from one to the other even if the coefficient of coupling is very low. Similarly, in quantum mechanics, an electron has a high probability of penetrating a potential barrier to occupy a level of the same energy on the other side. Thus the gaseous atom loses its electron and becomes ionized.

If $\Phi < E_i$, energy level (1) is below the Fermi level. The metallic energy levels of approximately the same energy are fully occupied and cannot possibly admit another electron. Thus ionization does not take place.

From the foregoing discussion, we see that the essential condition for resonance ionization is $\Phi > E_i$. This relation is fully satisfied with a tungsten cathode and cesium vapor. The work function for tungsten is 4.52 volts, and the ionization potential of a cesium atom is 3.89 volts.

4-4b. CONTROL OF THE DENSITY OF IONS

We next ask how many ions are needed? Obviously, in order to neutralize the electronic charge, the density of the positive ions should be the same as the density of electrons in transit. This, however, does not mean that the current I_p carried by the positive ions should be the same as the current I_e of the electrons. Assuming identical densities,

$$\frac{I_p}{I_e} = \frac{\overline{v_{x_p}}}{\overline{v_{x_e}}} \qquad (4\text{-}31)$$

where $\overline{v_{x_p}}$ and $\overline{v_{x_e}}$ are average forward velocities of the ions and electrons, respectively. Since the gas atoms reach the same temperature T_1 upon contact with the cathode before they are ionized, we have

$$\tfrac{1}{2} m_p \overline{v_{x_p}^2} = \tfrac{1}{2} m_e \overline{v_{x_e}^2}$$

$$\frac{\overline{v_{x_p}}}{\overline{v_{x_e}}} = \sqrt{\frac{m_e}{m_p}}$$

where m_p and m_e are the masses of the ion and the electron respectively. Equation (4–31) becomes

$$\frac{I_p}{I_e} = \sqrt{\frac{m_e}{m_p}} \qquad (4\text{–}32)$$

Assuming cesium vapor is used, the positive ion current is only a fraction of 1% of the electron current.

In order to supply this stream of positive ions, the required number of collisions of gas atoms on the cathode is at least I_p/e per second. Let n_g denote the density of gas atoms. The number of collisions per second is $n_g \overline{v_g} \sigma_e/4$, where $\overline{v_g}$ is the average velocity of a gas atom. Using these relations, the minimum density n_g is obtained

$$\frac{I_p}{e} \leq \frac{n_g \overline{v_g} \sigma_e}{4}$$

$$n_g \geq \frac{4 I_p}{e \overline{v_g} \sigma_e} = \frac{4 I_e}{e \overline{v_g} \sigma_e} \cdot \sqrt{\frac{m_e}{m_p}}$$

$$= \frac{4 J_e}{e \overline{v_g}} \cdot \sqrt{\frac{m_e}{m_p}} \qquad (4\text{–}33)$$

We note that the temperatures of the gas atoms and the positive ions are definitely not the same. The positive ions have just been in contact with the cathode and have the same temperature as the latter. The gas atoms are of a considerably lower temperature, T_g, and $\overline{v_g}$ is proportional to $\sqrt{T_g}$. Since the vapor pressure p_g is proportional to $n_g T_g$, Eq. (4–33) can be written as

$$p_g = K_g \sqrt{T_g} J_e \qquad (4\text{–}34)$$

For cesium vapor, the proportionality constant K_g is 4.12×10^{-6} mm of $H_g/{}^\circ K^{1/2}$ — amp/cm^2.

Equation (4–34) gives the minimum required vapor pressure. The performance is little affected, however, as long as p_g stays within a few times this minimum value. If $n_p > n_e$, a positive space charge is built up which tends to repel newly formed positive ions back to the cathode. Since the resonance phenomenon works both ways, there is a definite probability of a returned ion's regaining its lost electron. Thus, the fraction of ionized atoms is reduced until a balance in space charge is reached.

One neat way of controlling p_g is by control of the anode temperature. Since the gas atoms are partially condensed and deposited on the surface of the anode, p_g is simply the vapor pressure at T_g. Using this relation and Eq. (4–34), the proper anode temperature can be determined as a function

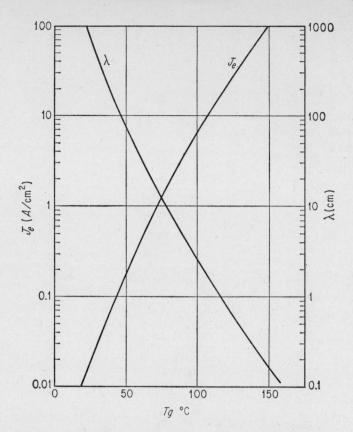

Fig. 4-9. THE MAXIMUM CURRENT DENSITY, $J:$, AND MEAN
FREE PATH, λ, OF ELECTRONS VERSUS VAPOR TEMPERATURE.
(Reprinted from K. G. Hernquist, M. Kaneksky, and F. H.
Norman, "Thermionic Energy Converters" *RCA Review*, Vol.
19, No. 2, June 1958, pp. 244–258.)

of J_c. For cesium vapor, this relation is plotted in Fig. 4-9. Also plotted
in Fig. 4-9 is the mean free path λ of electrons for the various vapor temperatures. It is noted that with a spacing between the electrodes of about
1 mm, the probability of collision of an electron in transit is very low.

4-4b. VOLTAGE, CURRENT CHARACTERISTICS

Due to the absence of appreciable space-charge effect, the potential distribution in a gas diode is that shown in Fig. 4-10. If $\Phi_a + V_0 < \Phi_c$, all
the emitted electrons from the cathode are absorbed by the anode. If

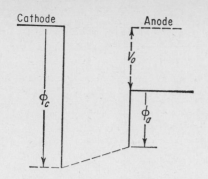

Fig. 4–10. ELECTRIC POTENTIAL DISTRIBUTION INSIDE A GASEOUS DIODE.

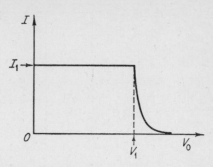

Fig. 4–11. RELATION BETWEEN LOAD CURRENT AND OUTPUT VOLTAGE, OF A GASEOUS DIODE. (Reprinted from K. G. Hernquist, M. Kanefsky, and F. H. Norman, "Thermionic Energy Converters" *RCA Review*, Vol. **19**, No. 2, June 1958, pp. 244–258.)

$\Phi_a + V_0 > \Phi_c$, only the electrons with sufficient forward kinetic energy succeed in reaching the anode. Therefore, the relationship between I and V_0 is that shown in Fig. 4–11. The output current I is a constant I_1 up to V_1, and then drops exponentially where

$$V_1 = \Phi_c - \Phi_a \qquad (4\text{-}35)$$

and

$$I_1 = I_e - I_p = \sigma_e J_e (1 - \sqrt{m_e/m_p}) \qquad (4\text{-}36)$$

Here J_e is the thermionic current density $A T_1^2 e^{-e\Phi_c/kT_1}$. The foregoing expectations agree very well with experimental results. For a gas diode with tungsten cathode and cesium vapor,

$$V_1 = 4.52 - 1.81 = 2.71 \text{ volts}$$

Experimental measurements show that I begins to drop as the load voltage exceeds 2.5 volts. The difference of 0.2 volt is accountable as the Seebeck emf of the external conductor, since most metals have negative thermoelectric power S.

4-4c. LOSS AND EFFICIENCY

The thermal input into a gas diode is essentially the same as that of a vacuum diode. The additional energy loss for ionizing the gas atoms is quite negligible because the required number of such ionizations is less than 1% of the number of electrons emitted. The heat convection due to gas atoms is also very low because the number of collisions with the cathode

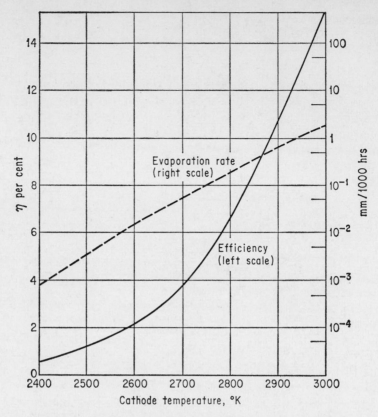

Fig. 4–12. Efficiency and Evaporation Rate of the Tungsten Cathode of a Diode Converter.

is of the same order of magnitude as the number of ionizations unless the vapor pressure (or anode temperature) is unduly high.

Because of the low anode temperature, the electrons emitted from the anode and the heat radiated from the anode are both negligible. Equations (4–20) and (4–21) become

$$q_e = J_e(\Phi_c + 2V_T) \tag{4–37}$$

$$q_r = \nu F T_1^4 \tag{4–38}$$

Neglecting heat loss and Seebeck effect due to the external conductors the total input is $\sigma_e(q_e + q_r)$. The output power is maximum if $V = V_1$. Therefore,

$$W = (\Phi_c - \Phi_a)\sigma_e J_e \left(1 - \sqrt{\frac{m_e}{m_p}}\right) \tag{4–39}$$

The efficiency is

$$\eta = \frac{W}{\sigma_e(q_e + q_r)} = \frac{(\Phi_c - \Phi_a)(1 - \sqrt{m_e/m_p})}{\Phi_c + 2V_T + \nu F T_1^2 A^{-1} e^{\Phi_c/V_T}} \qquad (4\text{–}40)$$

where V_T is kT_1/e. The efficiency for a tungsten-cesium vapor diode is plotted in Fig. 4–12. It is noted that the efficiency increases with cathode temperature. As the cathode temperature becomes higher, however, the rate of evaporation of the cathode material also rises rapidly. A compromise between operating life and efficiency must be made. As a reminder of this fact, the rate of evaporation of tungsten is plotted as a dashed curve on Fig. 4–12.

4-5. THE MAGNETIC TRIODE

Another way of overcoming the space-charge effect is by use of auxiliary acceleration and magnetic deflection. Referring to Fig. 4–13, the accelerating plate is connected externally to a high positive voltage source, and a strong magnetic field is applied in the perpendicular position (pointing into the paper). An emitted electron is first accelerated by the electric field and then bent toward the collector by the magnetic field. Assuming no collisions, while the voltage on the accelerating plate is high, no electron can reach it and consequently there is no current drain. As the kinetic energy of the electrons is high except at the beginning and end of their journeys, the space charge does not have much effect on their path.

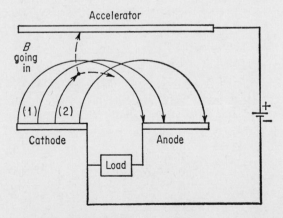

(1) Normal course

(2) Collision with another electron

Fig. 4–13. A Magnetic Diode and Typical Paths of Electrons.

The method is limited to a low current density because of the collision of electrons in transit. When two electrons collide, one of them is likely to be deflected toward the accelerating electrode. Thus there is a current drain in the high-voltage circuit, and the magnitude of this current is approximately proportional to the square of the emission current. The loss due to the current drain on the high voltage source prevents the magnetic diodes from being practical.

REFERENCES

1. Kaye, J., and J. A. Welsh, *Direct Conversion of Heat to Electricity*, chap. 1–11. New York: John Wiley & Sons, 1960.

2. Cadoff, I. B., and E. Miller, *Thermoelectric Materials and Devices*, chap. 4. New York: Reinhold Publishers, 1960.

3. Sproull, R. L., *Modern Physics*, pp. 364–78. New York: John Wiley & Sons, 1956.

4. Nottingham, W. B., *Thermionic Emission Handbuch der Physik*, vol. 21. Berlin: Springer-Verlag, 1956.

PROBLEMS

4–1. A high-vacuum type of thermionic converter has the following data:

     Spacing between electrodes $= 0.0015$ cm

                   $\Phi_0 = 2.4$ volts for both electrodes

     Operating temperature $= 2400°$K (cathode)

                        $450°$K (anode)

     Cathode and anode area $= 2.5$ cm^2

Calculate:

     (a) Current at critical output V_{0c} (Fig. 4–5)

     (b) E_p

     (c) Critical output voltage V_{0c}

4–2. In Prob. 4–1,

     (a) If the output voltage V_0 is

$$V_0 = V_{0c} + 0.5 \text{ volt}$$

     what is the output current?

     (b) Assume that the current is double its critical value with $V_0 = V_{0c} - 0.2$ volt, determine the new values of x_p and E_p.

4–3. The measured voltage vs. current values of a thermionic diode are given below:

V_0 (volts)	I (amperes)
1.5	55
2.0	10.0
2.5	0.5
3.0	0.025

What is the operating temperature of the cathode, assuming the anode to be cold?

4–4. A certain metal is used for both the anode and cathode material in a high-vacuumatic thermionic diode:

$$\nu = 0.01$$

$$\Phi = 3.75 \text{ volts}$$

(a) Calculate its figure of merit at $T = 1500°K$, $2000°K$, and $2500°K$; assume no space-charge effect.

(b) Calculate its efficiency when $T_{cathode} = 2000°K$, $T_{anode} = 1000°K$, for $V_0 = 0.5, 1, 1.5, 2$ volts. Assume that space charge is negligible.

4–5. A high-vacuum diode gives the following data:

Area of electrodes $= 14 \text{ cm}^2$
Spacing of electrodes $= 0.002 \text{ cm}$
Measured voltage current data

V_0	I
0.5	10
1.0	2
1.5	0.2
2.0	0.02

Determine:

(a) Cathode temperature

(b) Critical output voltage V_{0c}.

4–6. A high-vacuum diode is made with the following material:

Cathode	W	$\Phi_w = 4.52$
Anode	A	$\Phi_a = 2.60$

What is the open circuit voltage between cathode and anode if $T_c = 2800°K$, $T_a = 1150°K$? Neglect space charge.

4–7. A cesium diode is made with the same anode and cathode material as in Prob. 4–6 ($\Phi_{ce} = 1.81$ volts). Determine as closely as you can the output current versus voltage curve for the following two modes of operation:

(a) $T_{\text{cathode}} = 2800°\text{K}$
      $T_{\text{anode}} = 1150°\text{K}$
        $T_{\text{gas}} = 400°\text{K}$

The temperature of gas is lower owing to the existence of a condensing point at low temperature.

(b) $T_{\text{cathode}} = 2800°\text{K}$
      $T_{\text{anode}} = T_{\text{gas}} = 400°\text{K}$

The temperatures of gas and anode are identical because the gas condenses on the anode.

4–8. In Ex. 4–6, the calculations are approximate, as the equivalence itself is approximate. The exact open-circuit voltage can be calculated from Eq. (4–14) by letting $J_n = 0$ and evaluating V_0 from the resulting equation. The exact short-circuit current can also be calculated from Eq. (4–14) by letting $V_0 = 0$. Compare the approximate and exact values of open-circuit voltage and short-circuit current for

(a) Ex. 4–6
(b) For Ex. 4–6 with $T_{\text{anode}} = 2000°\text{K}$

CHAPTER FIVE

MAGNETOHYDRODYNAMIC ENGINES

Magnetohydrodynamic engines show promise as a way of generating electricity on a large scale, and are also being studied as rockets for the propulsion of spacecraft in interplanetary travel.

The primary objective of the present chapter is study of the energy-conversion process inside such a device. We begin by studying the basic principles involved in the conversion process itself and in the conduction of electricity through an ionized gas in the presence of a strong magnetic field. These are the basic subjects. We then proceed to give a mathematical analysis of the variations in pressure, density, temperature, and mean flow velocity of the gas as it progresses down the conversion chamber. The latter study is essential to an understanding of the limiting factors to the conversion effectiveness of an MHD engine.

5-1. A DESCRIPTION OF THE CONVERSION PROCESS

The principle of magnetohydrodynamic generators (or MHD generators for short) is quite simple. Suppose we apply a perpendicular magnetic field (pointing into the paper) to a charged particle moving at velocity v to the right as shown in Fig. 5-1. The magnetic force acting on the particle is

$$\mathbf{F} = q\mathbf{v} \times \mathbf{B} \qquad (5\text{-}1)$$

where **F**, **v**, and **B** are vectors, and **x** indicates vector product. If q is positive, the force acting on the particle points upward; if q is negative, the force acting on the particle points downward, as shown by the broken-line arrows in Fig. 5–1. Thus, the positively charged particle has a tendency of drifting toward plate P_1, and the negatively charged particle has a tendency of drifting toward plate P_2.

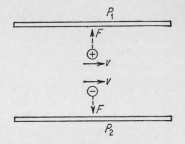

Now suppose instead of the two particles, we have a mass of ionized gas molecules moving at an average velocity v toward the right. The positive ions are accelerated toward plate P_1 and the negative ions are accelerated toward plate P_2. To be sure, the ions collide with the un-ionized molecules. Nevertheless, an average drift of the positive ions toward P_1 (and of negative

Fig. 5–1. Motions of Charged Particles in the Presence of a Perpendicular Magnetic Field.

ions toward P_2) is developed between collisions. If we connect plate P_1 to plate P_2 through an electrical load externally, a positive electric current will pass from P_1 through the load to P_2. This is the basic principle of the MHD generator.

Thus an MHD engine extracts mechanical energy from the mean flow of gas and converts it to electrical energy. The process is basically reversible.

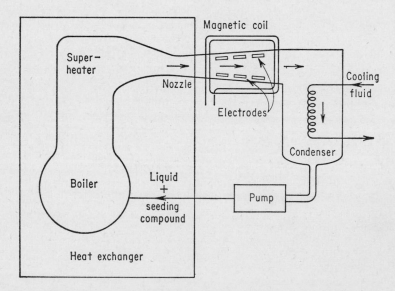

Fig. 5–2. The Basic Components of a MHD Generator.

If, instead of a load, we connect an external source of emf of sufficiently large magnitude in a direction opposite to the natural direction of current, the latter can be reversed, and energy fed into the mean flow.

Figure 5–2 illustrates the essential components of a MHD generator which converts heat into electrical energy in a closed cycle of operation. A superheated gas is expanded through a nozzle to obtain a high mean flow velocity. The ionization of the gas is accomplished by the natural process of thermal agitation and is sometimes aided by seeding into the gas a small amount of easily ionizable material or by using an RF field. The ionized gas is passed through the energy conversion chamber in which the generation of electricity takes place. Afterwards, the gas is condensed and pumped back into the boiler.

The reversed operation is illustrated by the MHD ramjet of Fig. 5–3. The inlet gas is accelerated as it passes through the conversion chamber and is ejected at a higher velocity.

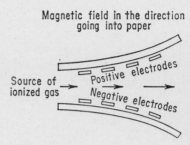

Fig. 5–3. A Longitudinal View of the Conversion Chamber of a MHD Generator.

5-2. TRANSFORMATION OF ELECTROMAGNETIC FIELDS

Perhaps the simplest as well as most rigorous way of analyzing the basic MHD process of generating electricity is through a study of the transformation of electromagnetic fields from a stationary reference system to a moving reference system.

As we know, physical quantities are defined through the ways of measuring them. How do we know there is an electric field? If we put a charged particle at rest in the field, we find there is a force acting on the charged particle, and the magnitude and direction of the force give the magnitude and direction of the electric field. How do we know there is a magnetic field? If we put a moving charged particle in the field, we find there is a force acting on the charged particle as given by Eq. (5–1). A student may ask: "Why not put a magnetic pole in the field instead of a moving charge?" We could do that also by using a very long thin magnet. But as the results of two ways of measuring the same physical quantity are obviously the same, there is no need to consider both.

The electromagnetic force acting on a moving charge is given as

$$\mathbf{F} = q(\mathbf{E} + \mathbf{v} \times \mathbf{B}) \tag{5-2}$$

With a single charged particle moving at a single $\mathbf{v}$, the six components of $\mathbf{E}$ and $\mathbf{B}$ cannot be determined from the three components of $\mathbf{F}$. By measuring the forces on particles moving at different $\mathbf{v}$'s, however, the vectors $\mathbf{E}$ and $\mathbf{B}$ can be completely determined. Thus, if we find the forces acting on charged particles moving at arbitrary $\mathbf{v}$'s to be given by

$$\mathbf{F} = q(\mathbf{X} + \mathbf{v} \times \mathbf{Y}) \tag{5-3}$$

we can safely say that

$$\mathbf{E} = \mathbf{X}$$
$$\mathbf{B} = \mathbf{Y} \tag{5-4}$$

Now let $\mathbf{E}$ and $\mathbf{B}$ represent the electromagnetic fields as seen in a stationary system, (measured by a laboratory setup which is at rest with respect to its special location on earth). Our problem is what are the values $\mathbf{E}'$ and $\mathbf{B}'$ measured by a laboratory setup which is moving at velocity $\mathbf{v}$? To answer this question, let us determine the force acting on a charged particle moving at velocity $\mathbf{v}'$ relative to the moving laboratory. Since the actual velocity (relative to the stationary system) is $\mathbf{v} + \mathbf{v}'$, the force is

$$\mathbf{F} = q[\mathbf{E} + (\mathbf{v} + \mathbf{v}') \times \mathbf{B}]$$
$$= q[\mathbf{E} + \mathbf{v} \times \mathbf{B} + \mathbf{v}' \times \mathbf{B}] \tag{5-5}$$

Applying Eq. (5–4) to the moving system gives

$$\mathbf{E}' = \mathbf{E} + \mathbf{v} \times \mathbf{B} \tag{5-6}$$
$$\mathbf{B}' = \mathbf{B} \tag{5-7}$$

In the foregoing derivation, we have not taken into account the more subtle relativistic effects, such as Lorentz contraction, etc., and Eq. (5–6) and Eq. (5–7) are not strictly correct. As we shall see later that $\mathbf{E}$ is of the order of $\mathbf{v} \times \mathbf{B}$ in MHD engines, Eqs. (5–6) and (5–7) differ from the exact Lorentz expressions by a term of the order of v^2/c^2, where c is the speed of light. In a typical MHD engine, the order of magnitude of v is around 1000 meters/sec. Thus

$$\frac{v^2}{c^2} = \frac{1000^2}{(3 \times 10^8)^2} = 10^{-11} \tag{5-8}$$

The error introduced by Eq. (5–6) and Eq. (5–7) is approximately one-billionth of 1%.

5-3. THE GENERATOR AND MOTOR EFFECTS OF AN MHD ENGINE

Now let us see the physical implications of Eq. (5–6) and Eq. (5–7). Referring to Fig. 5–4, an electric load of resistance R is connected across the

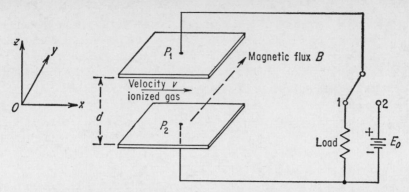

Fig. 5–4. An Idealized View of the MHD Conversion Process.

plates P_1 and P_2. A positive current I flows from plate P_1 through the load to plate P_2, and a voltage $V = RI$ is developed across the load. The electric intensity between the plates is

$$E_z = -\frac{V}{d} \tag{5-9}$$

where d is the distance between the plates.

To determine the effects the electromagnetic fields E_z and B have on the moving gas, let us imagine a laboratory moving with the gas. The gas is stationary as seen by the laboratory attendant. The electric and magnetic fields as seen by the attendant is

$$E'_z = E_z + Bv = \frac{1}{d}(Bvd - V)$$

$$B' = B \tag{5-10}$$

Now we shall make the following two observations:

(1) The physical laws as seen by the attendant in his moving laboratory are exactly the same laws as seen by us.

(2) The motions of various particles in the ionized gas constitute an objective fact. As such, it remains the same no matter who sees it.

The electromagnetic fields E_z and B acting on the moving gas produce exactly the same forces on the ions as electromagnetic fields E'_z and B acting on a gas with zero average velocity. The electric field E'_z can be produced by an emf E_i in series with the external voltage V as shown in Fig. 5–5, where

$$E_i = Bvd \tag{5-11}$$

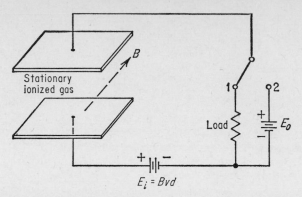

Fig. 5–5. EQUIVALENT CIRCUIT OF A MHD GENERATOR.

As far as any external measurements can determine, E_i is an internal emf of the engine.

A volume of ionized gas with zero average velocity behaves like a passive resistor to external measurements. The MHD engine has an internal emf E_i equal to Bvd and an internal resistance R_i equal to $d/\sigma A$.

The flow of current I causes a force

$$F = BId \qquad (5\text{–}12)$$

acting on the ions and is eventually transmitted to the entire gas through collision. Referring to Fig. 5–4, the current I in the gaseous medium is in the z direction, and F is in the minus x direction. The force F tends to slow down the mean flow of the gas or to cause the pressure to build up in the minus x direction. In any case, it extracts from the mean flow a mechanical energy equal to

$$Fv = BIdv = E_iI \qquad (5\text{–}13)$$

Equation (5–13) gives the energy balance in the conversion of mechanical to electrical energy.

The MHD engine is basically reversible. Suppose in Fig. 5–4 we connect the source of emf E_0 instead of the load by moving the switch arm to position 2. The equivalent situation is illustrated in Fig. 5–5 with the switch in position 2. If $E_0 > Bvd$, the direction of the current is reversed. Consequently, the direction of the force acting on the ions is also reversed. It tends to speed up the mean flow rather than to retard the latter. The ejected gas is at a much higher speed than the inlet gas. In the meantime, the reaction force acting on the magnet tends to push the MHD engine in the minus x direction. Thus the MHD engine acts like a jet engine, with the exception that the input is electrical energy rather than fuel.

The foregoing explains the basic process by which an MHD engine converts mechanical energy into electrical energy, and vice versa. Quantitatively it is a very rough theory, as it does not take into account two significant factors:

(1) The pressure, temperature, and mean flow velocity vary from point to point, and are functions of x. Otherwise there cannot be any energy change in the flow and consequently no energy conversion. Therefore, both the generated emf and the conductivity are functions of x.

(2) The conduction of electricity through a stationary gas is not unaffected by the presence of a strong magnetic field under certain conditions.

In subsequent sections, we shall make a more detailed study of the MHD engine, taking into account the variations of the factors mentioned in Item 1. In fact, it is only by considering these variations that we are able to determine the limitations of MHD engines. We shall also study the condition under which Item 2 is not significant. The fulfillment of this condition is necessary for a MHD engine to operate well.

Example 5–1: A MHD engine has the following data:

$$\text{Plate area} = 0.1 \text{ m}^2$$
$$\text{Distance between plates} = 0.2 \text{ m}$$
$$\text{Cross-flux density} = 1.2 \text{ webers/m}^2$$
$$\text{Average gas velocity} = 1000 \text{ m/sec}$$
$$\text{Gaseous conductivity} = 10 \text{ mho/m}$$

Determine the open-circuit voltage and the maximum power output.
The open-circuit voltage is given as

$$E_i = 1.2 \times 1000 \times 0.2 = 240 \text{ volts}$$

The internal resistance is

$$R_i = \frac{0.2 \text{ m}}{0.1 \text{ m}^2 \times 10 \text{ mho/m}} = 0.2 \text{ ohm}$$

$$P_{\max} = \frac{E_i^2}{4R_i} = 72{,}000 \text{ watts}$$

The foregoing calculations are only approximate, as both the conductivity and the average gas velocity vary not only with the distance x, but with the load current as well.

5-4. GASEOUS CONDUCTION AND HALL EFFECT

In this section, we give a brief description of the process of gaseous conduction with special emphasis on the effect due to the presence of a magnetic field. We shall limit our study to the case with a gas at rest, i.e., having zero mean velocity. The results can be applied to the general case by using the transformation of Sec. 5–2.

The problem of gaseous conduction has two essential aspects:

1. The ionization and recombination of electrons and ions
2. The average motion of charge carriers

The first aspect deals with the densities of charge carriers and the dependence of the densities on macroscopic conditions, such as composition, pressure, and temperature of the gas. The second aspect deals with the observable effects which are consequences of the motions of charge carriers, such as conductivity, Hall effect, etc.

5-4a. THE THREE VELOCITIES

Before studying the gaseous conduction in an MHD engine, we must make a clear distinction of the three types of motions of any single charge carrier:

(1) The *mean flow* is the average movement of the gas as a whole. The velocity of mean flow is denoted as $\mathbf{v}$.

(2) The thermal movement is the Brownian motion due to thermal agitation. Its velocity is denoted as $\mathbf{u}$.

(3) The drift motion is due to electromagnetic forces acting on a charged particle. Its average velocity is denoted as $\mathbf{u}_d$.

A neutral atom or molecule has only $\mathbf{v}$ and $\mathbf{u}$.

5-4b. THE IONIZATION PROCESS

When an orbital electron of a gas molecule acquires sufficient energy through thermal agitation (or to say it quantum mechanically, by absorbing a thermal photon), it escapes from the molecule and becomes a free electron. The remaining molecule becomes a positively charged ion. Sometimes, a molecule separates into a positive ion and a negative ion. At the same time, electrons and ions, or positive and negative ions, recombine into neutral molecules. Under conditions of equilibrium, the density (or number per unit volume) of ionized molecules satisfy

$$n_i = C n_0^{1/2} T^{3/4} e^{-\phi/2kT} \qquad (5\text{--}14)$$

where C is a proportionality constant, and ϕ is the energy deficiency which binds the electron to the rest of the atom, or the two ions together, and n_0 is the density of the un-ionized molecules. Assuming electrical neutrality on the average, the densities of positive and negative ions are identical and are both represented by n_i. Equation (5–14) is an approximation and holds only if $kT \ll \phi$, in which case n_i is small compared to n_0. As T increases, n_i increases sharply through the exponential dependence. At $kT = \phi$, a substantial number of molecules are ionized, and Eq. (5–14) no longer holds.

The physical processes which give rise to Eq. (5–14) can be described as follows: At all times the positive and negative ions collide with each other, and when a collision does take place there is a probability p_r that they recombine into a neutral molecule. The frequency of collision is pro-proportional to the densities of the ions and the speed or $\sqrt{T}$. Therefore, the rate of recombination is

$$R_r = C_1 n_i \cdot n_i \cdot p_r \sqrt{T}$$

In the meantime, the neutral molecules are dissociating into ions at a rate

$$R_d = C_2 n_0 p_d$$

The ratio p_d/p_r is proportional to $T^2 e^{-\phi/kT}$, which accounts for the probability of a molecule's acquiring the necessary energy ϕ to ionize through thermal agitation. Under equilibrium condition, $R_d = R_r$, and

$$n_i^2 = C^2 n_0 T^{3/2} e^{-\phi/kT}$$

Taking the square root of the foregoing expression gives Eq. (5–14).

A significant point about Eq. (5–14) is that it is not changed by the presence of other types of molecules. For instance, in a helium gas seeded with potassium, n_0 is the density of the potassium atoms. As helium is far more difficult to ionize, its presence is completely immaterial. With the same n_0, the same n_i is produced whether helium is present or not. This occurs because the number of collisions per second between electrons and potassium ions is not changed by the presence or pressure of helium.

The energy ϕ which binds a valence electron to an atom has a value of a few electron volts, whereas the energy ϕ which binds an innermost electron to a nucleus is proportional to the square of the nuclear charge, from a few electron volts for hydrogen to about 10^5 ev for the heaviest nuclei. Since $k = 8.616 \times 10^{-5}$ ev per degree, it takes a temperature of at least a few thousand degrees to cause substantial ionization of valence electrons from their molecules or atoms but much higher temperature to cause complete ionization of an atom.

A gas with a substantial number of ionized particles in it is one kind of *plasma*. There is no clear demarcation line of what is a plasma from what is not. It would be too inclusive to call a gas with any trace of charged particles in it a plasma. A gas without ions is yet to be found. We shall use the word *plasma* in the practical sense to mean a gas which has fairly high conductivity for electricity. As high conductivity is a necessary condition for an MHD engine to operate well, MHD engines are also called *plasma engines*.

Owing to material limitations, the temperatures of the electrodes and enclosures are limited to not much over 2500°K if not less. Consequently, the ionized gas is limited to about the same temperature, which is not high enough to cause sufficient ionization except in the most easily ionized gases. The alkali metals have a single valence electron in the outermost shell. It is very loosely bound to the rest of the atom, and the energy deficiency ϕ is small. For this reason, the ionized gases most commonly used in experimental MHD engines are either evaporated alkali metal or an ordinary gas seeded with a small trace of alkali metal. The seeding of an easily ionizable material helps to provide charge carriers directly, and the collision of free electrons with the bounded electrons of the host material also increases the percentage of ionization of the host material. A conductivity of about 10 mho per meter at 2000°K can be obtained by seeding air with about 1% of potassium vapor.

5-4c. GASEOUS CONDUCTION

Consider a high-temperature gas. The valence electrons of some gas molecules or atoms are dissociated from the rest of the atoms. The latter carries positive charge and is called a *positive ion*. Thus both types of charge carriers are usually present and the gas as a whole is neutral.

The charge carriers and neutral atoms or molecules move at high speed with the average kinetic energy of each particle in each degree of freedom equal to $\frac{1}{2}kT$:

$$\tfrac{1}{2}m\overline{u_x^2} = \tfrac{1}{2}m\overline{u_y^2} = \tfrac{1}{2}m\overline{u_z^2} = \tfrac{1}{2}kT \tag{5-15}$$

where m is the mass of the particle, and u_x is the velocity component in

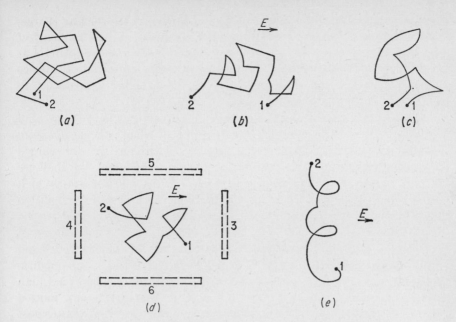

Fig. 5-6. Typical Paths of Electrons in a Gaseous Plasma: (a) In the Absence of any Electromagnetic Field; (b) Electric Field only; (c) Magnetic Field only; (d) Perpendicular Electric and Magnetic Fields are Present, Mean Free Path ≪ Mean Radius; (e) Perpendicular Electric and Magnetic Fields are Present, Mean Free Path ≫ Mean Radius.

the x direction, etc. We note from Eq. (5–15) that a lighter particle moves at higher velocity.

The motion of a particle is deflected every time it collides with another particle. Fig. 5–6(a) illustrates the typical random motion of a charge carrier in the absence of any external field. The particle starts at 1 and after some time ends at 2. On the average, the particle does not move much from its original position. Fig. 5–6(b) illustrates the situation in the presence of an electric field but without any magnetic field. Let us say that the charge carrier is an electron, and the electric field intensity E is pointing toward the right. There is an acceleration of the electron eE/m_e toward the left. Though the time between collisions is relatively short, and consequently the change in velocity of the electron in each leg of its journey may or may not be perceptible, there is definitely an average drift toward the left after many collisions. To be more quantitative, as the charge carrier starts off in an entirely new direction after each collision, the previously accumulated drift velocity is completely wiped out. Thus, the average velocity is simply the average accumulated drift velocity between collisions:

$$u_d = \frac{eE\tau}{2m_e} \tag{5-16}$$

where τ is the average interval between collisions.

Equation (5–16) shows that the drift velocity is proportional to E and the mobility of a charge carrier is defined as

$$\mu \equiv \frac{u_d}{E} \tag{5-17}$$

For electrons, it follows from Eq. (5–16)

$$\mu_e = \frac{e\tau}{2m_e} \tag{5-17a}$$

Let n_e denote the density of electrons. There are $n_e v_d$ electrons crossing a unit area and each of these electrons carries a charge e. The current density due to the drift of electrons is

$$J_e = en_e u_d = \frac{n_e e^2 \tau E}{2m_e}$$

Therefore, the conductivity due to electrons is

$$\sigma_e = \frac{J_e}{E} = \frac{n_e e^2 \tau}{2m_e} \tag{5-18}$$

Equation (5–18) also holds for positive ions with n_e, m_e, and τ replaced by n_i, m_i, and τ_i which are the density, mass, and average interval between collisions of positive ions respectively. As m_i for a hydrogen ion is about 1,800 times larger than m_e, and m_i for a cesium ion is more than 200,000 times larger than m_e, the conductivities due to positive ions are entirely negligible compared to the conductivity of electrons. We can regard σ_e as the conductivity of the gas and drop the subscript e in Eq. (5–18).

The average interval τ between collisions depends on the pressure and temperature of the gas. At a temperature up to a few thousand degrees K (depending on the gas), only a very small fraction of the gas molecules is ionized. Owing to the attraction between electrons and positive ions, however, the likelihood of a collision between an electron and a positive ion is much higher than that between an electron and a neutral particle. Though the positive ions are a small minority, they have decided influence on τ.

The likelihood of a collision is given a quantitative expression by the concept *collision cross section*. It is defined as an area A about the center of a particle such that a collision occurs as soon as the other particle comes within A. The area A is perpendicular to the relative motion of the two particles by definition.

Let A_0 and A_i denote the collision cross sections between an electron and a neutral particle and between an electron and a positive ion respectively. Let n_0 and n_i denote the densities of neutral particles and positive ions respectively. Suppose in a certain interval of time an electron has traveled a total distance L. The area A_0 has traced out a volume LA_0. The number of neutral particles inside this volume is n_0LA_0. Therefore, the number of collisions with neutral particles is n_0LA_0. Similarly, the number of collisions with positive ions is n_iLA_i. The average length of travel per collision is

$$l = \frac{L}{n_0LA_0 + n_iLA_i} = \frac{1}{n_0A_0 + n_iA_i} \tag{5-19}$$

In Eq. (5-19), l is the average length traveled by an electron between two collisions and is called the *mean free path* of electrons.

Let u_e denote the average speed of an electron. Then

$$\tau = \frac{l}{u_e} \tag{5-20}$$

and Eq. (5-18) becomes

$$\sigma = \frac{n_ee^2}{2m_eu_e} \cdot \frac{1}{n_0A_0 + n_iA_i} \tag{5-21}$$

Equation (5-21) has the following significance: In a gas in which electrons are the predominant form of negative ions, $n_e = n_i$, and both densities increase rapidly with the temperature according to Eq. (5-14). At relatively low temperature, the term n_iA_i is negligible compared to n_0A_0, and the conductivity σ rises with n_e. As the collision cross section A_i is approximately a few thousand times as large as A_0, however, it takes only an ion density of about 0.1% for the term n_iA_i to dominate. Therefore, both the numerator and denominator of Eq. (5-21) increases approximately in proportion to n_i as temperature rises, and the conductivity σ saturates at a value of $e^2/2m_eu_eA_i$.

To see the dependence of σ on gas pressure, let p_0 and p_i represent the partial pressures of neutral particles and ions respectively. Then

$$p_0 = n_0kT$$

$$p_i = n_ikT$$

$$p_e = n_ekT$$

Since

$$m_eu_e^2 = m_e\overline{u_x^2} + m_e\overline{u_y^2} + m_e\overline{u_z^2} = 3kT$$

Equation (5–21) becomes

$$\sigma_e = \frac{p_e e^2}{6(p_0 A_0 + p_i A_i)} \cdot \sqrt{\frac{3}{m_e k T}} = \frac{p_e e^2}{(p_0 A_0 + p_i A_i)} \cdot \sqrt{\frac{1}{12 m_e k T}}$$

In the preceding crude theory, we have been treating the averaged quantities rather loosely. A closer calculation gives

$$\sigma_e = \frac{2}{3} \frac{p_e e^2}{p_0 A_0 + p_i A_i} \cdot \sqrt{\frac{2}{\pi m_e k T}} \tag{5-22}$$

The only difference is in the constant coefficient.

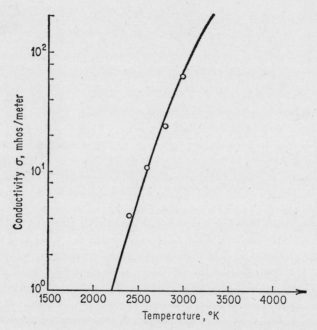

Fig. 5-7. A Comparison of Measured and Predicted Conductivity for Gas Seeded with 1% Potassium. (Reprinted from T. R. Brogan, J. F. Louis, R. J. Rosa, and Z. J. J. Stekly, "A Review of Recent MHD Generator Work at the Avco-Everett Research Laboratory," *AMP* **74,** Avco-Everett Research Laboratory, March 28, 1962.)

Figure 5–7 gives the conductivity of gas seeded with 1% potassium vapor in the temperature range of interest. The curves are obtained as a result of theoretical and experimental studies made at Avco Everett Research Laboratory. The solid lines are calculated results, which compare favorably with the experimental points obtained.

5-4d. THE HALL EFFECT

In the presence of magnetic field, the electrons no longer follow a straight-line path. There is no force in the direction of the magnetic field, and the motion is still a linear function of time. Figure 5–6(c) and Fig. 5–6(d) show the projection of the trajectory in a plane perpendicular to the direction of the magnetic field (the plane x-z in Fig. 5–4). In Fig. 5–6(c), E is assumed to be zero. As the magnetic force is perpendicular to the direction of motion, the projection of the trajectory between collisions is a circular arc. The radius of the arc is determined by the balance of magnetic force and centrifugal force:

$$\frac{m_e u_e^2}{r} = e u_e B$$

$$r = \frac{m_e u_e}{eB} \tag{5-23}$$

Except that the trajectory is an arc rather than a straight line between collisions, there is not much difference between Fig. 5–6(a) and Fig. 5–6(c). There is no drift or average motion of the electron.

Figure 5–6(d) shows the situation in the presence of an electric field, and the radius r is large compared to the mean free path l. The free electron path is actually a cycloid, but as the travel between collisions is small, it looks like a circular arc. The zigzagging trajectory is similar to that in Fig. 5–6(b). As the path between collisions is an arc instead of a straight line, however, the drift velocity toward the left is deflected upwards. As a result of this deflection, the equivalent flow of electric current is from upper left to lower right instead of from left to right. There is a definite angle of rotation of the direction of electric current from that of the electric field, and we may consider the conductivity σ as having an angle (equal to the angle of rotation) as well as magnitude. Thus in the presence of a magnetic field, the electric conductivity is a vector rather than a scalar.

A way of testing this effect is to place two pairs of plates as shown by the broken lines in Fig. 5–6(d). If we connect a voltage across plates 3 and 4 so that an electric field E is established as shown, the plate 5 will become negatively charged and the plate 6 will become positively charged. If we connect the plates together electrically, a positive current will flow from the bottom plate 6 to the top plate 5. This effect is called the *Hall effect*.

The Hall effect can be used to determine the nature of the charge carrier. Suppose in Fig. 5–6(d) the charge carriers are positively charged ions instead of negatively charged electrons. The ions describe counterclockwise arcs between collisions and drift from left to right on the average.

As the arcs are counterclockwise, the trajectories also deflect *upwards*. Thus, the equivalent electric current is from lower left to upper right. The plate 5 will become positively charged and the plate 6 will become negatively charged. Thus, the nature of the charge carriers can be determined from the polarity of the Hall effect.

Suppose we decrease the pressure or increase the magnetic flux density B so that the mean free path l is much longer than the radius r, the path of the electron (or other charge carrier) becomes that of Fig. 5–6(e). The electron follows a distinctively cycloid path in between collisions. Although it is not difficult to derive the shape of the trajectory between collisions mathematically, it is more instructive to see physically why this is so. As the magnetic force is always perpendicular to the path of an electron, it cannot increase or decrease the speed, nor transfer energy to, or from, the electron. The change of speed is due to the electric field alone. The conservation of energy requires that

$$\tfrac{1}{2}m_e u_e^2 + eEx = \text{constant}$$

and the electron moves faster when it is farther to the left. From Eq. (5–23) it is seen that r is proportional to v. Therefore, the instantaneous radius must be larger when the electrons are farther to the left. This explains qualitatively the trajectory of Fig. 5–6(e).

The practical significance of Fig. 5–6(e) is that with $l \gg r$ there is little or no drift velocity in the direction of the electric field, and consequently the electric conductivity is seriously reduced. In order to have an MHD engine operate properly, the conductivity of its ionized gas must be as high as possible. The Hall effect can be rendered insignificant by requiring

$$l < r$$

The significance of the foregoing requirement in terms of macroscopic variables will be derived presently. From Eq. (5–18) and Eq. (5–23)

$$\sigma = \frac{n_e e^2}{2m_e} \cdot \frac{l}{u_e} \leq \frac{n_e e^2}{2m_e u_e} \cdot \frac{m_e u_e}{eB} = \frac{n_e e}{2B} \tag{5–24}$$

As the density n, and partial pressure p are related to the temperature by

$$p = nkT$$

inequality (5–24) can be rewritten as

$$\sigma \leq \frac{p_e}{2BV_T} \tag{5–25}$$

where p_e is the partial pressure of the electrons, and $V_T = kT/e$.

Example 5-2: In a certain MHD engine, the operating gas temperature is 2500°K, and the gas conductivity is 20 mho/m. What is the least partial pressure of the electrons so that the Hall effect can be neglected in the presence of a magnetic flux density of 1.2 weber/m²? If only 0.02% of the gas molecules is ionized and practically all the negative ions are electrons, what is the minimum pressure of the gas?

SOLUTION: Equation (5–25) gives

$$p_e \geq 2BV_T\sigma = 2 \times 1.2 \times (2500 \times 8.616 \times 10^{-5}) \times 20$$

$$= 10.33 \text{ newton/m}^2$$

$$p_{gas} = 10.33 \div 0.0002 = 5.16 \times 10^4 \text{ newton/m}^2.$$

As 1 atmosphere pressure is 1.012×10^5 newton/m², the pressures cited can be written as

$$p_e = 1.02 \times 10^{-4} \text{ atm}$$

$$p_{gas} = 0.51 \text{ atm}$$

5-4e. SUMMARY

In the preceding sections, we have discussed the pertinent facts about gaseous conductivity. Now we shall give a brief summary of these facts:

(1) The conduction of electricity through a gaseous medium is accomplished by the motion of *charge carriers*, a term which includes the electrons and ions.

(2) An orbital electron in an atom (or molecule) is bound to the rest of the atom (or molecule) by an energy deficiency ϕ. It flies away as soon as it acquires an amount of energy in excess of ϕ through thermal agitation or other means. In the meantime, free electrons and ions recombine into neutral atoms (or molecules). The two processes arrive at a state of equilibrium.

(3) In order to cause an appreciable fraction of atoms (or molecules) to ionize, kT must be of the same order of magnitude as ϕ. Even for the valence electrons of the most loosely bound alkali metals, the required T is above 2000°K. Thus, only alkali metal vapors or other gas seeded with alkali metal vapors are used in experimental MHD engines.

(4) Except at very low pressures, the drift (or average) velocity of a charge carrier is small compared to its mean velocity of thermal motion. When this is true, the drift velocity, and consequently the convection electric current, is proportional to the electric field intensity **E**. Thus the conductivity of a gas can be defined.

(5) The conduction of electricity in a gas is almost entirely due to the free electrons because of their small mass and consequent high mobility.

(6) The gaseous conductivity increases with T at first because the density of free electrons increases with T. After 0.1% or more ions are present, the frequent collisions between ions and electrons reduce the mobility of the electrons and tend to keep the conductivity at a saturated value despite further increases in the density of electrons.

(7) In the presence of a strong magnetic field, the trajectory of a charge carrier between collisions is an arc. Consequently, the gaseous conductivity is a vector (or tensor) rather than a scalar, in the sense that the conduction current is not in the same direction as the electric field intensity. This is called the *Hall effect*.

(8) In the ultimate limit of having a mean free path much larger than the radius of the trajectory, the charge carriers move sideways, and the gaseous conductivity is seriously reduced.

(9) As a strong magnetic field is a necessity in an MHD engine, the pressure of the gas must be sufficiently high to keep the mean free path small, at least not larger than the radius of the trajectory. This requirement results in a lower limit for the partial pressure of electrons Eq. (5–25).

(10) In thyratrons, the ionization is accomplished by collisions of free electrons with bound electrons. In order that the free electrons may acquire sufficient energy before collision, the mean free path must be sufficiently large (pressure sufficiently low). This is not possible in MHD engines, since the mean free path must be short in order to offset the Hall effect. Thus, our only means of achieving high gaseous conductivity are reduced to the more brutal ones of high temperature and seeding.

5-5. DIMENSIONAL ANALYSIS

In this section, we study the effects of size on the performance of an MHD engine. *The mean velocity* v, *current density* J *and flux density* B *are assumed to be independent of size, and the MHD engines of various sizes are assumed to be proportional.* The purpose is to establish the trends of variation of the various terms entering into the energy-conversion process as the linear dimension of the engine is increased.

Let L denote a characteristic length of the engine; L may be the separation between the electrodes, or the cubic root of the total volume, etc. As the engines are assumed to be proportional, the exact choice of L is immaterial. Let us consider the terms one by one:

The Converted Power P

$$P = EI = Bvd \cdot JA = JBvK_1L^3$$

where K_1 is a constant independent of L.

The i²R *Loss inside the Plasma*

$$Q_p = \int \frac{J^2}{\sigma} d\tau = \frac{1}{\sigma} J^2 K_2 L^3$$

The Friction Loss at the Walls. The wall friction is a small fraction f of ρv^2 per unit area. Therefore, the total loss for a wall area A_w is

$$F = f\rho v^2 A_w \cdot v = K_3 v^3 L^2$$

The Heat Loss at the Walls. The heat loss at the walls depends on the allowed temperature of the wall material. If the allowed temperature of the material is considerably higher than the gas temperature, the heat generated at the walls due to friction can be carried away by the gas itself. In that case, the heat loss at the walls can be reduced to a negligible value by using adequate thermal insulation. If the allowed temperature of the material is equal to, or lower than, the gas temperature, external cooling must be used and the total heat loss is proportional to the area of the wall. Therefore, the heat loss H can be expressed as

$$H = K_4 L^2$$

The i²R *Loss of the Magnetizing Coil,* Q_m. A magnetizing coil of n turns with total copper cross section A_c and mean length per turn l has a resistance

$$R = \frac{\rho l n^2}{A_c}$$

where ρ is the resistivity of the wire material. Therefore,

$$Q_m = i^2 R = \frac{\rho l}{A_c} (ni)^2$$

Let l_m denote the length of the magnetic path. Then

$$ni = \frac{Bl_m}{\mu_0}$$

and consequently

$$Q_m = \frac{\rho l l_m^2}{A_c \mu_0^2} B^2 = \frac{\rho B^2}{\mu_0^2} K_5 L$$

The i^2R loss depends on L linearly, since l and l_m are proportional to L and A_c is proportional to L^2.

In the preceding equations, K_1, K_2, K_3, K_4, and K_5 are constants.

The significant points of the foregoing analysis are (1) the converted power is proportional to the volume of the engine; (2) for a sufficiently large MHD engine, the wall friction, loss of heat at the walls, and the i^2R loss in the magnetizing coil are small compared to the energy converted; (3) the i^2R loss in the plasma is proportional to the energy converted. Therefore, the MHD engine is efficient at high power levels but is rather inefficient at low power level. It is unlikely to be commercially feasible for any application below the 10- or 100-megawatt power level.

In the subsequent analysis, we assume the MHD engine to be sufficiently large so that the friction and loss of heat at the walls and the i^2R loss in the magnetizing coil can be neglected.

5-6. ANALYSIS OF A CONSTANT-AREA MHD ENGINE

In this section, we analyze the performance of a simplified version of an MHD engine. Referring to Fig. 5–4, the following assumptions are made

(1) The cross-sectional area of flow, A, between plates P_1 and P_2 is constant.

(2) The pressure p, average velocity v, and temperature T of the ionized gas are functions of x only. For steady flow, they are independent of t.

(3) The friction and heat loss at the walls are negligible.

(4) The flux density B is a constant. In reality, B varies slightly owing to the flow of electric current between P_1 and P_2. The variations are small and negligible, however, compared to the magnitude of B.

(5) The ionized gas follows the ideal gas law:

$$\frac{p}{\rho} = R_1 T \qquad (5\text{-}26)$$

where R_1 is the gas constant for 1 kg of gas, or the universal gas constant divided by the molecular weight.

In the analysis, we divide the conversion chamber into slices along the x direction in much the same way a baker slices his bread. Since the variables in each slice do not vary much, we assume that they can be treated as constants and the basic relations derived in Sec. 5–3 hold true in each slice of the conversion chamber.

5-6a. BASIC EQUATIONS

Figure 5–8 shows an enlarged portion of Fig. 5–4 between the plates P_1 and P_2. Let us consider the volume of gas bounded by two imaginary planes, P' and P'' at x_1 and x_2 respectively, which move with the mean flow. At a small interval δt second later, the two planes P' and P'' move to $x_1 + \delta x_1$, and $x_2 + \delta x_2$ respectively, where

$$\delta x_1 = v(x_1)\ \delta t$$

$$\delta x_2 = v(x_2)\ \delta t \qquad (5\text{-}27)$$

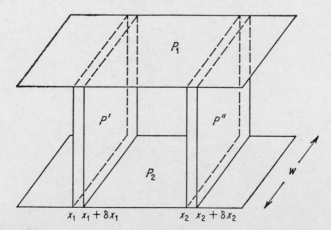

Fig. 5–8. Cross-sections of the Conversion Chamber Being Analyzed.

Let I_{12} denote the total current between x_1 and x_2. There are three conditions which must be satisfied by the motion of the volume of gas under consideration:

1. *Conservation of Matter*

Since the planes P' and P'' move with the mean motion, the total amount of matter bound between them does not change with time. Thus, the mass of gas bound between x_1 and x_2 is the same as the mass of gas bound between $x_1 + \delta x_1$ and $x_2 + \delta x_2$:

$$A \int_{x_1}^{x_2} \rho(x)\, dx = A \int_{x_1+\delta x_1}^{x_2+\delta x_2} \rho(x)\, dx$$

Subtracting from both sides the integral

$$A \int_{x_1+\delta x_1}^{x_2} \rho(x)\, dx$$

gives

$$A \int_{x_1}^{x_1+\delta x_1} \rho(x)\, dx = A \int_{x_2}^{x_2+\delta x_2} \rho(x)\, dx \tag{5-28}$$

As δx_1 and δx_2 can be made arbitrarily small by making δt small, Eq. (5–28) becomes

$$A\rho(x_1)\, \delta x_1 = A\rho(x_2)\, \delta x_2 \tag{5-29}$$

Combining Eq. (5–27) and Eq. (5–29) gives

$$A\rho(x_1)\, v(x_1) = A\rho(x_2)\, v(x_2) \tag{5-30}$$

Equation (5–30) shows that ρv is a constant independent of x. It is the mass flow rate q:

$$q \equiv A\rho v \tag{5-31}$$

2. *Conservation of Momentum*

Newton's second law states that the rate of change of momentum of a physical body is equal to the total force acting on it. For the mass of gas bound between P' and P'', we have the following quantities in the momentum equation:

Forces due to static pressure in the x *direction*

$$Ap(x_1) - Ap(x_2)$$

Magnetic force in the x *direction*

$$-BI_{12}\, d$$

Rate of change of momentum

$$\frac{A}{\delta t}\left[\int_{x_1+\delta x_1}^{x_2+\delta x_2} \rho(x)v(x)\ dx - \int_{x_1}^{x_2} \rho(x)v(x)\ dx\right]$$

$$= \frac{A}{\delta t}\left[\int_{x_2}^{x_2+\delta x_2} \rho(x)v(x)\ dx - \int_{x_1}^{x_1+\delta x_1} \rho(x)v(x)\ dx\right]$$

$$= \frac{A\rho(x_2)v(x_2)\ \delta x_2}{\delta t} - \frac{A\rho(x_1)v(x_1)\ \delta x_1}{\delta t}$$

$$= A[\rho(x_2)v^2(x_2) - \rho(x_1)v^2(x_1)]$$

Newton's second law gives

$$\rho(x_2)v^2(x_2) - \rho(x_1)v^2(x_1) = p(x_1) - p(x_2) - \frac{BI_{12}\ d}{A}$$

It can be written alternatively as

$$(p + \rho v^2)_{\text{at } x_2} = (p + \rho v^2)_{\text{at } x_1} - \frac{BI_{12}}{w} \tag{5-32}$$

where w is the width as shown in Fig. 5–8.

The expression $p + \rho v^2$ is called the *stagnation pressure* and will be denoted as p_s:

$$p_s \equiv p + \rho v^2 \tag{5-32a}$$

It is the pressure which develops at the stagnation point along a line of flow.

3. *Conservation of Energy*

Now we shall apply Eq. (2–1) to the volume of gas between P' and P''. Assuming that conduction of heat is negligible, we have

$$\Delta Q = 0 \tag{5-33}$$

In the temperature range of interest, the internal energy due to thermal motion is proportional to the temperature of the gas. Another part of the internal energy is the kinetic energy attributed to the mean flow. For a slice of gas of thickness dx, the total internal energy is

$$dU = \rho A\ dx(C_{v1}T + \tfrac{1}{2}v^2)$$
$$\quad\ \ \text{mass}\quad\ \text{thermal}\quad\text{kinetic}$$

where C_{v1} is the specific heat at constant volume for 1 kg of gas. The total internal energy for the volume of gas between P' and P'' is the integral of the foregoing expression. The increase in internal energy is

$$\Delta U = \int_{x_1+\delta x_1}^{x_2+\delta x_2} dU - \int_{x_1}^{x_2} dU = \int_{x_2}^{x_2+\delta x_2} dU - \int_{x_1}^{x_1+\delta x_1} dU$$

$$= A\rho(x_2)\ \delta x_2 [C_{v1} T(x_2) + \tfrac{1}{2} v^2(x_2)] \tag{5-34}$$

$$- A\rho(x_1)\ \delta x_1 [C_{v1} T(x_1) + \tfrac{1}{2} v^2(x_1)]$$

The work done by the gas is partly electrical and partly mechanical. The electrical output is

$$VI_{12}\ \delta t$$

Where V is the voltage between the plates P_1 and P_2. The mechanical work done by the gas is

$$Ap(x_2)\ \delta x_2 - Ap(x_1)\ \delta x_1$$

The total work done by the gas is

$$\Delta W = VI_{12}\ \delta t + Ap(x_2)\ \delta x_2 - Ap(x_1)\ \delta x_1 \tag{5-35}$$

Substituting Eqs. (5-33) to (5-35) into Eq. (2-1) and dividing the resulting expression by δt give

$$q\left[C_{v1} T(x_2) + \frac{p(x_2)}{\rho(x_2)} + \frac{1}{2} v^2(x_2) \right] + VI_{12}$$

$$= q\left[C_{v1} T(x_1) + \frac{p(x_1)}{\rho(x_1)} + \frac{1}{2} v^2(x_1) \right] \tag{5-36}$$

Equation (5-36) has a simple physical explanation. The quantity

$$q\left(C_{v1} T + \frac{p}{\rho} + \frac{1}{2} v^2 \right) = h_T \tag{5-37}$$

is the enthalpy of the mass of gas q which flows across the cross section at x every second. To see this, let M denote the molecular weight of the gas in kilograms. The internal energy U of the gas has a random component and a component due to the kinetic energy of mean flow v:

$$U = mC_v T + \tfrac{1}{2} qv^2$$

$$= \frac{qC_v T}{M} + \frac{1}{2} qv^2 = qC_{v1} T + \frac{1}{2} qv^2$$

As the volume occupied by the gas is

$$V = \frac{q}{\rho}$$

Eq. (5–37) can be rewritten as

$$h_T = U + pV$$

Comparing the preceding expression of h_T with Eq. (2–15), it becomes apparent that h_T is simply the enthalpy H of the amount of gas which flows across the cross section at x per second. Consequently it is called the *enthalpy flux* in the literature.

Physically, the *enthalpy flux* is the rate of flow of total energy across a given surface. We note that, as the amount of gas q flows across the cross section at x, it carries with it its thermal energy $qC_{v1}T$ and kinetic energy (of mean flow) $qv^2/2$. The term

$$\frac{qp}{\rho} = Apv$$

represents the rate of mechanical work done across the cross section by hydraulic pressure because Ap is the force due to hydraulic pressure, and v is the velocity.

The enthalpy flux h_T can be expressed in various other ways. Note that the constant pressure specific heat C_{p1} is given as

$$C_{p1} = R_1 + C_{v1} \tag{5–38}$$

and the ratio γ is defined as

$$\gamma = \frac{C_{p1}}{C_{v1}} \tag{5–39}$$

From Eq. (5–26), h_T can be written as

$$h_T = q(C_{v1}T + R_1T + \tfrac{1}{2}v^2)$$
$$= q(C_{p1}T + \tfrac{1}{2}v^2) \tag{5–40}$$

Alternatively,

$$h_T = q\left(\frac{C_{v1}}{R_1} \cdot \frac{p}{\rho} + \frac{p}{\rho} + \frac{1}{2}v^2\right)$$

$$= q\left(\frac{\gamma}{\gamma - 1}\frac{p}{\rho} + \frac{1}{2}v^2\right) \tag{5–41}$$

Using the concept of enthalpy flux, Eq. (5–36) can be written as

$$h_T(x_1) - h_T(x_2) = VI_{12} \tag{5–42}$$

The conservation of energy is demonstrated by Eq. (5–42). The electrical output is equal to the rate of total energy flowing in at x_1 minus the rate of total energy flowing out at x_2.

Another equation gives the current I_{12} as a function of the gas variables. Since σ and v are functions of x, the current density J is also a function of x. From Eq. (5-10),

$$J(x) = \sigma(x) E_z'(x) = \sigma(x) \left[Bv(x) - \frac{V}{d} \right] \qquad (5\text{-}43)$$

$$I_{12} = \int_{x_1}^{x_2} w J(x)\, dx = w \int_{x_1}^{x_2} \sigma(x) \left[Bv(x) - \frac{V}{d} \right] dx \qquad (5\text{-}44)$$

The significances of the equations derived in this section are summarized as follows:

(1) Equations (5-26), (5-31), (5-32), (5-42), and (5-44) give a complete description of the conversion process. Given any set of initial conditions p, ρ, v, T, and I_{12} at $x = x_1$, the subsequent values of these variables are completely determined. As the choices of x_1 and x_2 are completely arbitrary, we may choose x_1 to be at the inlet end, $x_1 = 0$, and let the value of x_2 range from the inlet to the outlet end, $x_2 = x$, $0 \le x \le l$. The solutions of the five equations give p, ρ, v, T, and I_{0x} as functions of x.

(2) The conductivity σ affects only the distance of travel x for the gas to arrive at any given state, but does not affect the eventuality of that state. For instance, for a certain conductivity, I_{0x} is 100 amp at $x = 0.2$ and p, ρ, v, T become p_1, ρ_1, v_1 and T_1 respectively. For a higher conductivity, I_{0x} is 100 amp at $x = 0.1$. Then at $x = 0.1$, p, ρ, v, and T are still p_1, ρ_1, v_1, and T_1. This is so because, once I_{0x} is given, $p(x)$, $\rho(x)$, $v(x)$, and $T(x)$ are completely determined from I_{0x} and the initial values $p(0)$, $\rho(0)$, and $v(0)$, and $T(0)$ through Eq. (5-26), Eq. (5-31), Eq. (5-32), and Eq. (5-42). The conductivity determines only the value of x necessary to accumulate a current equal to I_{0x}.

5-6b. CONVERSION EFFECTIVENESS

The conversion effectiveness of an MHD engine is the ratio of the electric power output to the enthalpy flux at the input end:

$$\eta_c \equiv \frac{V I_{0l}}{h_T(0)} \qquad (5\text{-}45)$$

where I_{0l} is the total conduction current between the two plates P_1 and P_2. We denote the input plane as $x = 0$ and the output plane as $x = l$.

From Eq. (5–42), Eq. (5–45) can be written as

$$\eta_c = \frac{h_T(0) - h(l)}{h_T(0)} = 1 - \frac{h_T(l)}{h_T(0)} \tag{5–46}$$

We note that $h_T(0)$ is the total gaseous power input to the MHD engine, and $h_T(l)$ is the unused gas power at the exhaust end. The conversion effectiveness is quite similar to the thermal efficiency defined in Sec. 2–4.

5-6c. NORMALIZED EQUATIONS

The first step in solving complicated physical equations is usually reducing them to normalized form. For each variable in the equation, we find a natural unit which is written in terms of constants of the problem. By expressing the variables in their natural units, the equations are reduced to much simpler forms. The set of equations derived in Sec. 5–6a will be solved presently by using this principle. Equation (5–31) can be used to eliminate the variable ρ in Eq. (5–32a) and Eq. (5–41):

$$p_s = p + \frac{qv}{A} \tag{5–47}$$

$$h_T = \frac{\gamma}{\gamma - 1} Apv + \frac{1}{2} qv^2 \tag{5–48}$$

A natural unit for v is

$$v_0 \equiv \frac{V}{dB} \tag{5–49}$$

At a mean flow speed $v = v_0$, the generated emf Bvd is just sufficient to balance out the terminal voltage V and no current will flow. It is not obvious what unit should be used for p. We can normalize the v terms in Eq. (5–47) and Eq. (5–48) first and see what happens. Multiplying Eq. (5–47) and Eq. (5–48) by A/qv_0, and $1/qv_0^2$ respectively, we obtain

$$\frac{Ap_s}{qv_0} = \frac{Ap}{qv_0} + \frac{v}{v_0} \tag{5–50}$$

$$\frac{h_T}{qv_0^2} = \frac{\gamma}{\gamma - 1} \cdot \frac{Ap}{qv_0} \cdot \frac{v}{v_0} + \frac{1}{2}\left(\frac{v}{v_0}\right)^2 \tag{5–51}$$

From Eq. (5–50) and Eq. (5–51), the natural unit for p is seen to be qv_0/A. It is the rate of momentum flow per unit area at a mean flow speed

v_0. The per unit variables P_s, H, P, and Q are defined as

$$P_s \equiv \frac{Ap_s}{qv_0} \qquad P \equiv \frac{Ap}{qv_0}$$

$$H \equiv \frac{h_T}{qv_0^2} \qquad Q \equiv \frac{v}{v_0} \tag{5-52}$$

Using the per unit variables, Eq. (5–50), Eq. (5–51), Eq. (5–32), Eq. (5–42), and Eq. (5–46) can be written as

$$P_s = P + Q \tag{5-53}$$

$$H = \frac{\gamma}{\gamma - 1} PQ + \frac{1}{2} Q^2 \tag{5-54}$$

$$P_s(0) - P_s(x) = \frac{ABI_{0x}}{qv_0 w} = \frac{VI_{0x}}{qv_0^2} \tag{5-55}$$

$$H(0) - H(x) = \frac{VI_{0x}}{qv_0^2} \tag{5-56}$$

$$\eta_c = 1 - \frac{H(l)}{H(0)} \tag{5-57}$$

In Eq. (5–55) and Eq. (5–56), we have set $x_1 = 0$ and $x_2 = x$.

5-6d. THE STAGNATION PRESSURE VERSUS ENTHALPY DIAGRAM

Equations (5–53) to (5–57) can be readily solved with the aid of the P_s-H diagram of Fig. 5–9. In the diagram, P_s is used as the y coordinate and H is used as the x coordinate. The following points become apparent:

(1) For each given Q, the locus of (H, P_s) traces out a straight line as P varies.

(2) The envelope of the family of straight lines with different values of Q is a parabola. The equation of the parabola is given as a solution to the following two equations:

$$\delta P_s = \delta P + \delta Q = 0$$

$$\delta H = \frac{\gamma}{\gamma - 1} (P\,\delta Q + Q\,\delta P) + Q\,\delta Q = 0$$

These equations can be satisfied (except for the trivial solution $\delta Q = \delta P = 0$) only if

$$
-\begin{vmatrix} 1 & 1 \\[2ex] \dfrac{\gamma}{\gamma - 1} P + Q & \dfrac{\gamma}{\gamma - 1} Q \end{vmatrix} = \frac{\gamma}{\gamma - 1} P - \frac{1}{\gamma - 1} Q = 0
$$

The solution is

$$
Q = \gamma P \tag{5-58}
$$

On the P_s-H diagram, an equation between P_s and H is obtained by eliminating Q and P from Eq. (5–53), Eq. (5–54), and Eq. (5–58):

$$
H = \frac{\gamma^2}{2(\gamma^2 - 1)} \cdot P_s^2 \tag{5-59}
$$

(3) The envelope of the constant Q lines has the following physical significance: As

$$
\frac{Q}{\gamma P} = \frac{1}{\gamma} \cdot \frac{q v_0}{A p} \cdot \frac{v}{v_0} = \frac{\rho v^2}{\gamma p} = \frac{v^2}{a^2} = M^2 \tag{5-60}
$$

where a is the velocity of sound $\sqrt{\gamma p / \rho}$, and M is the Mach number. The envelope is the sound barrier where the mean flow velocity v is equal to the velocity of sound.

(4) Each constant Q line is divided by its tangential point on the sound barrier into two segments. The lower segment represents supersonic speeds; the upper segment represents subsonic speeds. This is proved as follows: Consider any point L on the lower segment of a constant line and the tangential point T of the same line,

$$
P_s(L) < P_s(T), \qquad Q(L) = Q(T)
$$

$$
P(L) < P(T)
$$

Therefore,

$$
\frac{Q}{\gamma P(L)} > \frac{Q}{\gamma P(T)} = 1 \tag{5-61}
$$

Since $Q/\gamma P(L)$ is equal to the ratio v^2/a^2 at L, it follows from inequality (5–61)

$$
\left(\frac{v^2}{a^2} \right)_{\text{at } L} > 1 \tag{5-62}
$$

(5) The sound barrier divides the P_s-H plane into two regions: The region below the sound barrier is physically inaccessible. In order to obtain a pair of values (H, P_s) below the sound barrier, the mean flow velocity v must be complex. Above the sound barrier, each point (H, P_s) has two solutions for Q, one larger than γP and one smaller than γP.

(6) From Eq. (5–55) and Eq. (5–56), it is seen that as I_{0x} increases with x, the representative point $H(x)$, $P_s(x)$ traces out a straight line with unity slope toward the lower left corner on the P_s-H diagram. The locus of $H(x)$, $P_s(x)$ is called the *trajectory* of the MHD engine. An example is the trajectory AA' in Fig. 5–9.

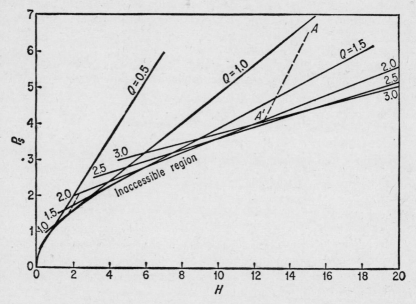

Fig. 5–9. STAGNATION PRESSURE VERSUS ENTHALPY DIAGRAM, $\gamma = 5/3$.

(7) From the trajectory, we can read the values of Q as x increases, representing the progress of the plasma down the engine. Although there are two solutions of Q for each point on the P_s-H diagram, there can be no ambiguity in the correct Q to use. Since the change in Q must be continuous, the gas stays supersonic if it starts out to be supersonic. It stays subsonic if it starts out to be subsonic.

(8) The length of the trajectory depends, of course, on the length of the engine and the conductivity of the gas. There are, however, two natural

boundaries which the trajectories cannot cross: one is the sound barrier. Obviously, the representative point cannot cross over the sound barrier into the inaccessible region and give complex values of Q. Physically, if the conversion chamber is sufficiently long to cause this, the flow becomes unstable and none of our previous analysis of a steady flow applies. The engine becomes inoperative or rather inefficient. The other is the $Q = 1$ line. Once this line is approached, the forces (on the charge carriers) due to electric and magnetic fields balance out and the current density J drops to zero. No matter how large x becomes, I_{0x} remains constant.

(9) The conductivity of the gas can affect only the correspondence between x and the length of the trajectory. It cannot change the position of the trajectory. The performance of an MHD engine with constant cross section can be calculated from the initial and final points on the trajectory without knowing σ.

(10) Using Eq. (5–57), the conversion effectiveness can be calculated directly from the H values at the starting and end points of the trajectory. The other variables are determined as follows:

  (a) P_s and Q are read from the P_s-H diagram.
  (b) P is calculated as $P_s - Q$.
  (c) The actual variables are calculated from P and Q as

$$p = \frac{qv_0}{A} \cdot P$$

$$v = v_0 \cdot Q$$

$$\rho = \frac{q}{Av_0} \cdot \frac{1}{Q} \tag{5–63}$$

$$T = \frac{v_0^2}{R_1} \cdot QP$$

(11) Since a trajectory is either supersonic or subsonic but is never mixed, Fig. 5–9 can be separated into two diagrams. Fig. 5–10 gives the supersonic P_s-H diagram and Fig. 5–11 gives the subsonic P_s-H diagram for a gas with $\gamma = 5/3$. It is noted that the speed of a supersonic gas reduces as the gas progresses, whereas the speed of a subsonic gas increases as the gas progresses down the conversion chamber.

(12) For operation as a jet, $Q < 1$, and the representative point moves on a straight line inclined at 45° from lower left to upper right.

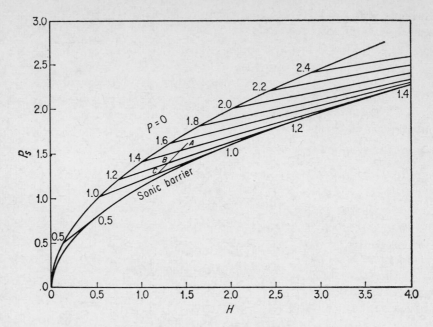

Fig. 5–10. Stagnation Pressure versus Enthalpy Diagram, Supersonic Region.

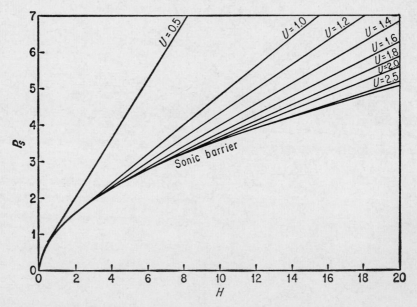

Fig. 5–11. Stagnation Pressure versus Enthalpy Diagram, Subsonic Region.

Example 5-3: An MHD generator with constant cross section uses argon seeded with 1% cesium as its working gas. The following data are given

$$d = 15 \text{ cm}$$

$$w = 10 \text{ cm}$$

$$B = 0.9 \text{ weber/m}^2$$

entering gas condition

$$T = 2500°\text{K}$$

$$p = 0.5 \text{ atm}$$

$$v = 2800 \text{ m/sec}$$

The output voltage is 250 volts. In order to assure reasonably uniform current density, it is required that the generated emf at every section be no less than 300 volts.

Determine the conversion effectiveness, power generated, and the condition of the gas at the outlet. Assume the average conductivity to be 100 mho/m and estimate the length of the conversion path.

SOLUTION: In order to use the P_s-H diagram, we shall calculate the mass flow rate q and the Mach number first. The gas is obviously monatomic with a molecular weight $= 40$. Therefore,

$$R_1 T = \frac{8310}{40} \times 2500 = 5.19 \times 10^5 \text{ joules/kg}$$

$$a^2 = \gamma R_1 T = \tfrac{5}{3} \times 5.19 \times 10^5 = 8.67 \times 10^5 \text{ joules/kg}$$

$$a = 932 \text{ m/sec}$$

$$M = \frac{2800}{932} = 3.0$$

$$v_0 = \frac{V}{Bd} = \frac{250}{0.9 \times 0.15} = 1850 \text{ m/sec}$$

$$q = A\rho v = \frac{Apv}{R_1 T}$$

$$= \frac{0.015 \times 5.06 \times 10^4 \times 2800}{5.19 \times 10^5} = 4.09 \text{ kg/sec}$$

$$qv_0^2 = 1.4 \times 10^7 \text{ watts}$$

$$\text{Entering } Q = Q(0) = \frac{2800}{1850} = 1.51$$

$$\text{Exit } Q = Q(l) = \frac{300 \text{ volts}}{250 \text{ volts}} = 1.2$$

$$\text{Entering } P = \frac{Q}{\gamma M^2} = \frac{1.51}{15} = 0.101$$

$$P_s(0) = 1.51 + 0.10 = 1.61$$

$$H(0) = \tfrac{5}{2} \times 0.101 \times 1.51 + \tfrac{1}{2} \times 1.51^2 = 1.52$$

The calculated $P_s(0)$ and $H(0)$ determine a point A on Fig. 5–10. Draw a straight line downward from A at a 45° angle. It intersects the $Q = 1.2$ line at B. The exit conditions of the gas are given by the point B:

$$P_s(l) = 1.39 \qquad H(l) = 1.29$$

$$P(l) = 1.39 - 1.2 = 0.19$$

Conversion effectiveness

$$\eta_c = 1 - \frac{1.29}{1.52} = 15.1\%$$

Power generated

$$W = qv_0^2[H(0) - H(l)] = 1.4 \times 10^7 \times 0.23 = 3.22 \times 10^6 \text{ watts}$$

Condition of gas at outlet

$$T = T(0) \times \frac{P(l)Q(l)}{P(0)Q(0)} = 2500 \times \frac{0.19 \times 1.2}{0.10 \times 1.51} = 3770°\text{K}$$

$$P(l) = 0.5 \text{ atm} \times \frac{0.19}{0.101} = 0.94 \text{ atm}$$

$$v(l) = 1850 \times 1.2 = 2220 \text{ m/sec}$$

Length of conversion path

$$\text{Output current: } I = \frac{3.22 \times 10^6}{250} = 12900 \text{ amp}$$

$$\text{Average voltage: } \frac{378 + 300}{2} = 339 \text{ volts}$$

$$\text{Conductance: } K = \frac{12900}{339 - 250} = 145 \text{ mho}$$

Length of conversion path

$$K = \frac{\sigma l w}{d}$$

Therefore,

$$l = \frac{Kd}{\sigma w} = \frac{145 \times 0.15}{100 \times 0.1} = 2.2 \text{ m}$$

Example 5-4: What is the maximum conversion effectiveness of the MHD generator of Ex. 5–3 if there is no limit to the length of the conversion path?

SOLUTION: If there is no limit to the length of the conversion path, energy conversion can take place as long as the generated emf is greater than 250 volts; in other words, as long as $Q > 1$.

Extend the line AB in Fig. 5–10 until it intersects the $Q = 1$ line at C. The point C gives $H(l) = 1.18$.

$$\eta_c = 1 - \frac{1.18}{1.52} = 22.3\%$$

5-7. MHD ENGINES WITH VARYING CROSS SECTION AND MAGNETIC FIELD INTENSITY

The limitations on the conversion efficiency can be largely overcome by allowing B and the cross section of the conversion chamber to vary in such a way that Bvd is essentially constant as v approaches a preselected final value. The detailed analysis is quite involved and is beyond the scope of this book. Referring to Fig. 5–12, we confine ourselves to a discussion of the factors governing the conversion process of such a machine.

(1) Conservation of matter still holds. In Eq. (5–31), the mass flow rate q is a constant, but the cross-sectional area A is a function of the coordinate x.

(2) Conservation of momentum is no longer a useful relation. As the walls are not parallel to x, the reaction of the walls to gas pressure has a component in the direction of x. Equation (5–32) is no longer valid.

(3) Conservation of energy is still true, and Eq. (5–42) can be used without modification.

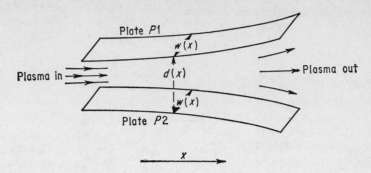

Fig. 5–12. A Conversion Chamber with Varying Cross-sections.

(4) Equation (5–32) is replaced by an equation giving the entropy rise due to I^2R loss in the plasma. A more practical way to represent the entropy relation is as follows: There are two components of energy associated with the gas: the kinetic energy of mean flow and the internal energy. The kinetic energy of mean flow does not have any entropy associated with it and can be ignored in the calculation of entropy. Furthermore, as our ultimate purpose is to find a relation on the state variables p, ρ, and T to replace Eq. (5–32), we can make our calculations in terms of these variables directly.

Let Q represent the total I^2R loss in the plasma as it travels from $x = 0$ to $x = l$. Then the heating per kilogram of gas is Q/q. Equation (2–10) gives

$$\frac{dQ}{q} = C_{V1}\, dT + p\, dV = C_{V1}\, dT - p\, \frac{d\rho}{\rho^2} \tag{5–64}$$

As an approximation let it be assumed that the heating rate is proportional to temperature increment. Then,

$$\frac{1}{q} \cdot \frac{dQ}{dT} = \frac{Q}{q[T(l) - T(0)]} = C_q \tag{5–65}$$

where C_q is a constant. Equation (5–64) can be written as

$$(C_{V1} - C_q)\, dT - R_1 T\, \frac{d\rho}{\rho} = 0 \tag{5–66}$$

Integrating Eq. (5–66) from 0 to l gives

$$\left(\frac{T(l)}{T(0)}\right)^{(C_{v1}-C_q)/R_1} = \frac{\rho(l)}{\rho(0)} \tag{5-67}$$

Equation (5–67) together with Eq. (5–31) and Eq. (5–42) can be used to estimate the performance as well as the ratio of the inlet to outlet cross-sectional areas of an MHD engine. The limit on conversion efficiency is set by Eq. (5–42) and Eq. (5–40). Obviously $T(l)$ and $v(l)$ should be as small as possible to reduce $h_T(l)$. As $T(l)$ must be sufficiently high to give adequate conductivity, however, and $v(l)$ must be sufficiently high to generate the required emf, there is a lower limit of $h_T(l)$.

Once $T(l)$ and $v(l)$ are selected, the conversion effectiveness and generated power can be calculated, and Q can be estimated. Given Q and $T(l)$, the ratio $\rho(l)/\rho(0)$ is determined from Eq. (5–67) and the area ratio is determined from Eq. (5–31).

From practical considerations, it is desirable to have the same coils magnetizing the whole length of the conversion path. Furthermore, the generated emf, E, should be constant so that uniform voltage drop in the conversion chamber can be maintained. The generated emf, E, and the mmf, F, are two constants of the MHD engine. We assume further that the magnetic path external to the conversion chamber can be made of magnetic material, and that the wall thickness of the conversion chamber is proportional to w. Under these assumptions,

$$B = \frac{K_b F \mu_0}{w} \tag{5-68}$$

where K_b is a constant less than 1. From Eq. (5–11) and Eq. (5–31)

$$E = Bvd = \frac{K_b F \mu_0 vd}{w} \tag{5-69}$$

$$q = w \, d\rho v \tag{5-70}$$

Multiplying Eq. (5–69) by Eq. (5–70) gives

$$v^2 d^2 \rho = \frac{qE}{K_b F \mu_0} = K_7 \tag{5-71}$$

Dividing Eq. (5–70) by Eq. (5–69) gives

$$w^2 \rho = \frac{q K_b F \mu_0}{E} = K_8 \tag{5-72}$$

Equations (5-71) and (5-72) can be rewritten as

$$d = \frac{1}{v}\sqrt{\frac{K_7}{\rho}} \tag{5-73}$$

$$w = \sqrt{\frac{K_8}{\rho}} \tag{5-74}$$

Example 5-5: An MHD generator with variable cross section has the same inlet dimensions and entering gas condition as Ex. 5-3. By varying d and w with x and using a weaker magnetizing coil, the generated emf is kept at 300 volts throughout the conversion path. The condition of the gas at the outlet is

$$T(l) = 2000°\text{K}$$

$$v(l) = 1400 \text{ m/sec}$$

Calculate

  (a) Conversion effectiveness
  (b) Output electric power
  (c) Pressure of the gas at the outlet
  (d) Outlet dimensions
  (e) Flux densities at the inlet and outlet.

SOLUTION: Instead of calculating the numerical values directly, we shall find expressions of the conversion effectiveness and C_q of Eq. (5-67) in terms of dimensionless parameters. Let

$$\alpha = \frac{T(l)}{T(0)}$$

$$\beta = \frac{v(l)}{v(0)}$$

$$\lambda = \frac{E}{V}$$

Then,

$$h_T = q\left(\frac{\gamma}{\gamma - 1} R_1 T + \frac{1}{2} v^2\right) = q\left(\frac{\gamma}{\gamma - 1} R_1 T + \frac{M^2}{2} \gamma R_1 T\right)$$

$$= \frac{\gamma q R_1 T}{\gamma - 1}\left[1 + \frac{M^2}{2}(\gamma - 1)\right]$$

Therefore,

$$h_T(0) = \frac{\gamma q R_1 T(0)}{\gamma - 1} \left[1 + \frac{M^2(0)}{2} (\gamma - 1) \right]$$

$$h_T(l) = \frac{\gamma q R_1 T(0)}{\gamma - 1} \left[\alpha + \frac{\beta^2 M^2(0)}{2} (\gamma - 1) \right]$$

$$\eta_c = 1 - \frac{h_T(l)}{h_T(0)} = \frac{1 - \alpha + (1 - \beta^2) M^2(0) (\gamma - 1)/2}{1 + M^2(0) (\gamma - 1)/2} \qquad (5\text{--}75)$$

$$Q = EI - VI = VI \left(\frac{E}{V} - 1 \right) = VI(\lambda - 1)$$

$$= h_T(0) \eta_c (\lambda - 1)$$

$$C_q = \frac{Q}{q[T(l) - T(0)]} = - \frac{\gamma \eta_c (\lambda - 1)}{(\gamma - 1)(1 - \alpha)} \left[1 + \frac{M^2(0)}{2} (\gamma - 1) \right] R_1$$

$$(5\text{--}76)$$

For the example in question,

$$\alpha = \frac{2000}{2500} = 0.8$$

$$\beta = \frac{1400}{2800} = 0.5$$

$$\lambda = \frac{300}{250} = 1.2$$

$$\eta_c = \frac{0.2 + 0.75 \times 9 \times \frac{2}{3} \times \frac{1}{2}}{1 + 9 \times \frac{2}{3} \times \frac{1}{2}}$$

$$= \frac{2.45}{4} = 0.6125$$

$$C_q = - \frac{5}{2} \times 0.6125 \times \frac{0.2}{0.2} \times 4R_1 = -6.125R_1$$

(a) $\eta_c = 61\frac{1}{4}\%$

(b) $VI = h_T(0) \eta_c = 1.4 \times 10^7 \times 1.52 \times 0.6125 = 1.3 \times 10^7$ watts

(c) $\dfrac{\rho(l)}{\rho(0)} = \left(\dfrac{2000}{2500}\right)^{1.5+6.125} = 0.8^{7.625} = 0.183$

$\dfrac{p(l)}{p(0)} = \dfrac{\rho(l)}{\rho(0)} \cdot \dfrac{T(l)}{T(0)} = 0.8 \times 0.183 = 0.146$

$p(l) = 0.5 \text{ atm} \times 0.146 = 0.073 \text{ atm}$

(d) Outlet dimensions

$w = 10 \text{ cm} \times 0.183^{-1/2} = 23.4 \text{ cm}$

$d = 15 \text{ cm} \times 0.183^{-1/2} \times 2 = 70.2 \text{ cm}$

(e) $B(0) = \dfrac{300}{0.15 \times 2800} = 0.714 \text{ weber/m}^2$

$B(l) = \dfrac{300}{0.702 \times 1400} = 0.305 \text{ weber/m}^2$

By comparing the results of Ex. 5–3 and Ex. 5–5, we see that an MHD generator with constant cross section operating in the supersonic range tends to compress and heat up the gas. As the kinetic energy is partly used up in compressing the gas, the conversion effectiveness is necessarily low. This difficulty is not basic, however, as it can be removed by increasing the cross section with x in a predetermined manner.

For subsonic operation, a large part of the input enthalpy is contained in the internal energy of the gas. The temperature of the gas must reduce in order to supply the output energy. As the i^2R heating of the plasma is also there, however, the gas must expand in order to absorb this heat energy and to end at a lower temperature as well. As $A\rho v_1$ is a constant, decreasing ρ means increasing v, and part of the internal energy is converted into kinetic energy instead of into useful output. Therefore the conversion effectiveness is also low. The difficulty can be avoided by making $A(x)$ an increasing function of x.

The same principles apply to MHD jets, except that $E < V$ and I is negative in Eq. (5–42). The i^2R heating of the plasma causes the gas to expand as before, and an MHD jet is not the *reversible* process of an MHD generator.

A significant factor which we have neglected in Sec. 5–6 and Sec. 5–7 is the *turbulence flow* of the working gas. It has been assumed that the mean flow is a function of x, and consequently the i^2R loss in the plasma is due to the load current only. In the presence of turbulent flow, short-circuit electric currents or *"eddy" currents* are induced in the plasma. The entropy of the plasma is further increased by an amount independent of the load current. Its practical effect is an increase in Q of Eq. (5–65) and further expansion of the working gas.

5-8. CONCLUSION

MHD generators are most suitable for large-scale generation of direct current power. In principle, they are quite similar to conventional generators, especially unipolar generators. Instead of driving a metallic conductor across a magnetic field, a mass of ionized gas is driven across a magnetic field, whereby it generates electricity in a direction perpendicular to both the magnetic field and the motion.

The method is attractive because, in respect to equipment, it offers an efficient and potentially inexpensive way to generate electricity. There is no moving component and consequently no mechanical wear. The ionized gas can be recirculated indefinitely. *The basic problem which will eventually determine the usefulness of this method is that of finding a material which will stand high temperature. Because of Hall effect limitations, it is not possible to reduce the gas pressure to a value where ionization by collision can be effective. The only means at our disposal, then, are seeding and high temperature. In order to obtain a 2000°C gas at high velocity, the initial temperature at the superheater must be much higher.*

This chapter gives the basic principle of MHD engines and the closely related topic of gaseous conduction. In the last part of the chapter, MHD engines with constant and variable cross sections are analyzed. The purpose of the analysis is showing the significant factors involved, rather than giving exact calculations of the performance of the MHD engines. An MHD generator with constant cross section tends to heat the gas unnecessarily if it is operating in the supersonic range, or to speed the gas unnecessarily if it is operating in the subsonic range. Both effects limit its conversion effectiveness. These limitations can be lifted by increasing the cross section of the MHD generator with x.

REFERENCES

1. Sproull, R. L., *Modern Physics*, pp. 24–45. New York: John Wiley $\dot{m}$ Sons, 1956.

2. Kaye, J., and J. A. Welsh, *Direct Conversion of Heat to Electricity*, pp. 12-1–13-12. New York: John Wiley $\dot{m}$ Sons, 1960.

3. Neuringer, J. L., "Optimum Power Generation Using a Plasma as a Working Fluid," *Third Biennial Gas Dynamics Symposium*. Evanston, Ill.: Northwestern University Press, 1960, pp. 153–67.

4. Coe, W. B., and C. L. Eisen, "The Effect of Variable Plasma Conductivity on MHD Energy Converter Performance," *Elect. Eng.*, December, 1960, pp. 997–1004.

5. Rosa, R. J., and A. R. Kantrowitz, "Magneto-hydrodynamic Energy Conversion Techniques," *Research Report* 86, Avco Everett Research Laboratory, Everett, Mass., April, 1959.

6. Lamb, L., and S. C. Lin, "Electrical Conductivity of Thermally Ionized Air Produced in a Shock Tube," *Research Report* 5, Avco Everett Research Laboratory, Everett, Mass., February, 1957.

7. Kantrowitz, A. R., T. R. Brogan, R. J. Rosa, and J. F. Louis, "The Magneto-hydrodynamic Power Generator—Basic Principles, State of the Art, and Areas of Application," *IRE Trans.* Vol. **MIL**-6 No. 1, January, 1962, pp. 78–83.

PROBLEMS

5-1. The load condition of an MHD generator can be represented by a ratio α:

$$\alpha \equiv \frac{E_i - V}{E_i}$$

Thus α is the ratio of internal voltage drop to generated emf. Express the output power and retarding force of the MHD generator of Ex. 5–1 in terms of α.

5-2. A MHD jet has the following given data:

Distance between electrodes	0.3 m
Conductivity	50 mho/m
Mean flow velocity	2000 m/sec
Area of electrodes	0.2 m^2
Applied voltage	1000 volts

At what field intensity is the power converted into mechanical power a maximum? What value is this maximum power?

5-3. The MHD generator principle is used for measuring mean flow velocity. Assume a distance of 1 cm between electrodes and a magnetic field of

$$B = 0.1 \sin 1000t \text{ weber/m}^2$$

At what flow velocity is the output voltage 1 microvolt rms? What is the inherent limitation of this method in terms of the type of fluid it can be used on?

5-4. For a given gas at constant density, how does the Hall effect vary with temperature? With the percentage of seeding?

5-5. The Hall effect angle θ_H is the angle between the electric field intensity vector **E** and the current density vector **J**.

(a) Show that, for small values of θ_H,

$$\theta_H = \frac{l}{2r}$$

(b) Referring to Fig. 5-6(d), the distance between plates 3 and 4 is d_1 and the distance between plates 5 and 6 is d_2. A voltage V is applied across plates 3 and 4. Find an expression for the open-circuit voltage across plates 5 and 6 in terms d_1, d_2, and θ_H.

5-6. An MHD engine can be viewed as a conversion device with three types of energy in it: thermal, mechanical, and electrical. Draw an energy-conversion diagram which is an enlargement of the one shown in Fig. 2-8 and find the proper locations for the various terms discussed in Sec. 5-5.

5-7. Recalculate Ex. 5-3 with B changed to 1.2 weber/m².

5-8. An MHD generator with constant cross section uses helium seeded with 1% potassium as its working gas. The following data are given

$$d = 25 \text{ cm}$$
$$w = 10 \text{ cm}$$
$$B = 1.2 \text{ weber/m}^2$$

entering gas condition

$$T = 3000°\text{K}$$
$$p = 1.0 \text{ atm}$$
$$v = 1000 \text{ m/sec}$$

The output voltage is 250 volts. In order to prevent instability, the Mach number is required to be 0.9 or under everywhere in the conversion chamber. Determine the conversion effectiveness, power generated, and the condition of the gas at the outlet. Assume the average conductivity to be 50 mho/m and estimate the length of the conversion path.

5-9. An MHD generator with variable cross section has the same inlet dimensions and entering gas condition as Prob. 5-8. By varying d and w with x, the generated emf is kept at 300 volts throughout the conversion path. The condition of the gas at the outlet is

$$T(l) = 2000°\text{K}$$
$$v(l) = 800 \text{ m/sec}$$

Calculate

(a) Conversion effectiveness
(b) Output electric power
(c) Pressure of the gas at the outlet
(d) Outlet dimensions

5–10. The MHD generator of Ex. 5–3 is used as a jet with an entering gas temperature of 2000°K and speed of 1000 m/sec. The applied voltage is 250 volts and everything else remains unchanged. Determine

(a) The limiting speed at the outlet
(b) The exit gas temperature for (a)
(c) The electrical power input for (a)

5–11. Find the limiting expression for $\rho(l)/\rho(0)$ of Eq. (5–67) in which $T(l) = T(0)$ but Q of Eq. (5–65) is a constant.

CHAPTER SIX

PHOTOVOLTAIC EFFECT
AND SOLAR CELLS

Photovoltaic cells are the most efficient means of generating electricity from solar energy. They accomplish their functions by converting the energies of photons directly into electricity. The life span of a photovoltaic cell is practically unlimited. Its power capacity per unit weight is also very high.

This chapter emphasizes the basic theory, operating characteristics, and factors affecting the efficiency and applicability of these devices.

6-1. THE ENERGY OF A PHOTON

As discussed in Sec. 2–12, one of the most fundamental concepts of modern physical science is the proposition that wave and particle can be two aspects of the same thing. An electromagnetic wave is a shower of photons, with each photon having its indivisible energy and momentum. A beam of sunlight is the superposition of electromagnetic waves of different frequencies and is, therefore, a shower of photons of assorted sizes (different energies and momentum).

The energy E of each photon is directly proportional to its frequency ν.

$$E = h\nu \tag{6-1}$$

where h is Planck's constant 6.6252×10^{-34} joule sec. Equation (6–1) can be written in different forms. One of the most commonly used forms is to

177

express the energy in electron volts:

$$E = eV = h\nu = \frac{hc}{\lambda}$$

Therefore,

$$V = \frac{hc/e}{\lambda} = \frac{12398 \text{ Å}}{[\lambda]} \text{ volts} \tag{6-2}$$

where Å stands for the angstrom unit of 10^{-10} m and $[\lambda]$ means wavelength in Å. One angstrom unit is approximately the dimension of one atom and is the most commonly used unit of length in the study of X rays and light. An easy way to remember Eq. (6–2) is to write

$$V = \frac{12345 \text{ Å}}{[\lambda]} \text{ volts} \tag{6-2a}$$

which is accurate enough for most engineering purposes. The constant 12398 Å has the significance of being the wavelength of a photon with an energy of 1 ev.

The term *photon flux* means the number of photons crossing a unit area perpendicular to the light beam per second. Let it be denoted by N. Let Φ denote the intensity of the light beam in watts per square meter. Then N is the number of photons with a total energy of Φ joules. For a monochromatic light beam,

$$N = \frac{\Phi}{h\nu} = \frac{\Phi\lambda}{hc} = 5.04 \times 10^{14}\Phi[\lambda]/\text{watts} - \text{Å} \tag{6-3}$$

Example 6–1: A monochromatic light beam has a wavelength of 5890 Å and an intensity of 0.5 watt/m². Calculate (a) energy of each photon in electron volts, (b) the photon flux of the beam, and (c) the photon density of the beam.

SOLUTION: For (a), Eq. (6–2) gives

$$V = \frac{12398}{5890} = 2.10 \text{ volts}$$

The photon energy is 2.10 ev.

For (b), Eq. (6–3) gives

$$N = 5.04 \times 10^{14} \times 0.5 \times 5890 = 1.485 \times 10^{18}/\text{m}^2$$

For (c), the photon density is

$$\rho = \frac{N}{c} = 4.95 \times 10^{9}/\text{m}^3$$

6-2. JUNCTION DIODES

A photovoltaic cell is a specially made junction diode so designed that a large fraction of the photons of the incident light beam are absorbed near the p-n junction. In order to understand its principle of operation, one must first understand the junction diodes.

Figure 6–1(a) illustrates the energy levels of a diode at the vicinity of the p-n junction. As discussed in Sec. 3–11, at zero current the diffusion of electrons from one side of the junction to the other and vice versa must be at equal rate, and this condition is realized if, and only if, the Fermi level E_0 is lined up all the way across the junction.

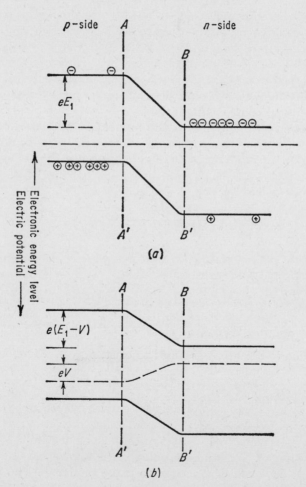

Fig. 6–1. Energy-level Diagram of a Junction Diode. (a) Under Equilibrium Condition;   (b) Forward Biased.

The detailed balance of electron and hole currents is established as follows: Consider the flow of electrons and holes out of the p side across section A. As electrons are minority carriers on the p side, the density of electrons is low and consequently relatively few electrons go across section A. As the electrons go downhill from A to B, however, practically all these electrons get across to B. There are many more holes which go across section A. As the holes are going uphill, however, only the small fraction $e^{-eE_1/kT}$ with energy eE_1 or more succeed in reaching B. The roles of electrons and holes are reversed in the flow of these particles out of the n side across section B. Let

I_1 = electron current from p side to n side,
I_2 = hole current from p side to n side,
I_3 = electron current from n side to p side,
I_4 = hole current from n side to p side,
n_1 = density of electrons at the p side,
n_2 = density of holes at the p side,
n_3 = density of electrons at the n side,
n_4 = density of holes at the n side,
I = net current flow from p side to n side.

Then

$$I_1 = k_1 n_1$$

$$I_2 = k_2 n_2 e^{-eE_1/kT}$$

$$I_3 = k_3 n_3 e^{-eE_1/kT}$$

$$I_4 = k_4 n_4$$

where k_1, k_2, k_3, and k_4 are constants.

$$I = -I_1 + I_2 + I_3 - I_4$$

$$= -(k_1 n_1 + k_4 n_4) + (k_2 n_2 + k_3 n_3) e^{-eE_1/kT}$$

As a condition of balance is assumed to exist, $I = 0$. Therefore,

$$k_1 n_1 + k_4 n_4 = (k_2 n_2 + k_3 n_3) e^{-eE_1/kT} \qquad (6\text{--}4)$$

If a positive voltage V is applied to the p side, the energy level diagram becomes that of 6-1(b). I_1 and I_4 are not changed as electrons going from A to B and holes going from B to A are still going downhill. A larger fraction, however, $e^{-e(E_1-V)/kT}$ of holes going from A to B and electrons going from B to A have sufficient energy to make the climb. The net current becomes

$$I = -(k_1 n_1 + k_4 n_4) + (k_2 n_2 + k_3 n_3) e^{-e(E_1-V)/kT} \qquad (6\text{--}5)$$

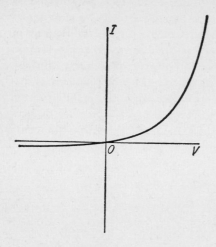

From the same reasoning, Eq. (6–5) is obviously correct also for negative values of V. With negative V of sufficient magnitude, the second term of Eq. (6–5) is negligible, and

$$I = -(k_1n_1 + k_4n_4) = -I_0 \quad (6\text{–}6)$$

The current I_0 is the maximum reversed current. Using Eq. (6–4) and Eq. (6–6), Eq. (6–5) can be written as

$$I = I_0(e^{eV/kT} - 1) \quad (6\text{–}7)$$

Fig. 6–2. CURRENT OF A JUNCTION DIODE VERSUS APPLIED VOLTAGE.

Equation (6–7) is the operating equation of a junction diode. A plot of I versus V is illustrated in Fig. 6–2. The rectifying function is clearly exhibited.

6-3. THE PHOTOVOLTAIC EFFECT

Figure 6–3 illustrates the situation when a light beam of sufficient energy $(h\nu > eE_g)$ falls upon the vicinity of a p-n junction. Since the atomic dimension is very small, the interaction of an electron is with an individual photon, and we may look upon the light beam as a shower of photons. A photon may "collide" with a free electron, a valence electron, or a hole and transfer its energy to the latter. Even in the most heavily doped semiconductors, however, the concentration or density of majority carriers is no more than $10^{26}/m^3$. This is about 1/10,000 of the density of valence electrons. Thus the probability of a photon colliding with a free carrier and transferring its energy to a free carrier is entirely negligible.

What happens then is a photon collides with a valence electron and the latter acquires an energy of eE_g or more by absorbing the former and becomes free. Figuratively speaking, an electron in the valence band is knocked into the conduction band and a hole is left behind. As illustrated in Fig. 6–3, this "pair creation" process may occur at different places along the junction. If it occurs in between sections A and B where there is a strong potential gradient as indicated by 1, the freed electron is accelerated by the potential to the n side and the hole is accelerated to the p side. The equivalent transfer of charge is that of a positive charge from n side to the p side. If the electron-hole pair is created on the n side as indicated

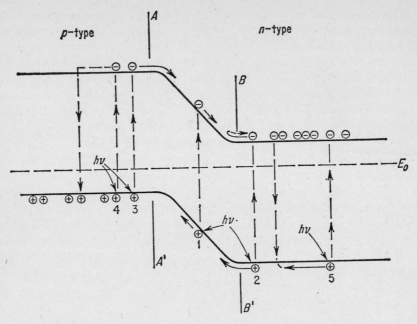

Fig. 6–3. THE PHYSICAL MECHANISM OF GENERATING PHOTO-
VOLTAIC CURRENT.

by 2, and the minority particle (the hole) drifts toward the junction, it gets
across to the p side and again a positive charge is transferred from n side
to the p side. The direction of movement of the majority particle is immaterial, as it generally does not have sufficient energy to climb the hill.
If the electron-hole pair is created on the p side as indicated by 3 and the
electron drifts toward the junction, it gets across to the n side and again a
positive charge is transferred from n side to the p side. Of course, it is also
possible for the created minority particles to drift away from the junction
and to combine eventually with a majority particle as illustrated by 4 and
5 of Fig. 6–3. No flow of charge across the junction will then result.

When a hole collides with a free electron, the probability that they
bounce away from each other is many times larger than the probability of
a recombination, or capture. A minority particle makes many collisions
and moves randomly as shown in Fig. 5–6(a) for a while before it is cap-
tured. If, during the period of random motion, it drifts into the depleted
region at the junction, the strong electric field does the rest and sends it
across the junction. The initial direction of the drift is unimportant. As
long as the minority particle is created close enough to the junction, its
probability of drifting across the junction is very high.

The closeness of the minority particle to the junction is measured in terms of *diffusion length, l,* which is the average net distance traveled by a minority particle before it recombines with a majority particle. The probability that the creation of an electron-hole pair at a distance d from the junction results into the flow of a positive charge from the n region to the p region is $e^{-d/l}$. Therefore, the diffusion length l is also the effective range in which an absorbed photon is likely converted into an electric current across the junction. Typical values of l are about 10^{-6} to 10^{-4} m, depending on carrier concentrations and the way the crystal is formed.

The preceding discussion points out two conditions which must be met for effective utilization of photon-generated current: First, the p-n junction must be effectively exposed to the light source. Second, provision must be made to collect and conduct the photovoltaic current to an external load. A device which realizes the foregoing requirements is illustrated in Fig. 6–4. Boron is diffused into a heavily doped n-type silicon

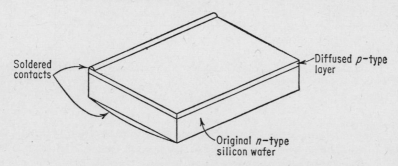

Soldered contacts

Diffused *p*-type layer

Original *n*-type silicon wafer

Fig. 6–4. Essential Parts of a Solar Cell.

wafer, and a p type skin of a few microns thick is formed on the top. Electric contact is made to the top and bottom by first nickel plating the surfaces and then soldering at the places shown in Fig. 6–4. The electrical load is connected across the soldered contacts. When light strikes the top surface, a positive electric current flows from the top contact through the load to the bottom contact.

The number of photons absorbed and converted into electricity can be determined by measuring the external current while keeping the two soldered contacts at the same potential. Figure 6–5 shows the result of such a measurement with monochromatic light beam at various wavelengths. Also shown are calculated total response and n-layer and p-layer responses. At short wavelengths there are fewer photons for the same light intensity, Eq. (6–3), and consequently the response is proportionally lower. At long wavelengths, the photon energy is too low to knock an electron in the

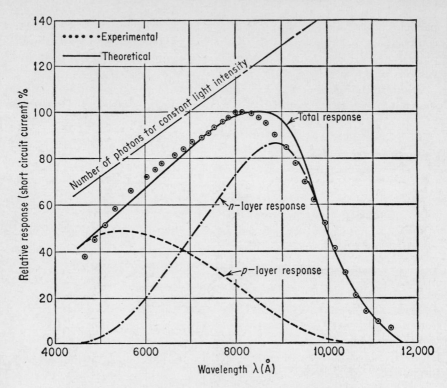

Fig. 6–5. CARRIER CREATION WITHIN A SOLAR CELL. (Reprinted from M. B. Prince and M. Wolf, "New Developments in Silicon Photo-voltaic Devices" *The Journal of the British Institution of Radio Engineers*, Vol. **18,** pp. 583–594, October 1958.)

valence band to the conduction band. Note that the energy gap of silicon is 1.1 ev, and consequently the cut-off wavelength is

$$\lambda_c = \frac{12{,}398}{1.1} = 11271 \text{ Å}$$

which agrees very well with Fig. 6–5. The maximum relative response occurs at a wavelength of approximately three-fourths of the cutoff wavelength.

6-4. OPERATING CHARACTERISTICS OF A PHOTOVOLTAIC CELL

With the two terminals of a photovoltaic cell short-circuited, the short-circuit current I_s is due to the diffusion of photon-generated minority particles across the junction. For a light beam of given color or frequency composition, I_s is proportional to the light intensity. Although the currents I_1, I_2, I_3, and I_4 as defined in Sec. 6–1 are also present, their total value is zero and they do not contribute to the external current.

Now if the external short circuit is replaced by an external load as shown in Fig. 6–6(a), a voltage V is developed across the load. The voltage

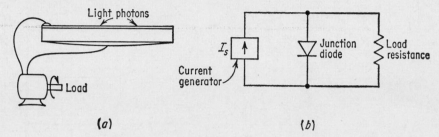

Fig. 6–6. SOLAR CELL AS D-C GENERATOR.

V lowers the potential difference across the junction and a larger proportion of majority particles succeed in getting across the junction. Thus I_2 and I_3 are increased. The minority currents I_1, I_4, and I_s remain unchanged, however, as long as the minority particles are still going downhill across the junction. The external load current is

$$I_L = I_s + I_1 + I_4 - I_2 - I_3$$

$$= I_s - I_0(e^{eV/kT} - 1) \qquad (6\text{--}8)$$

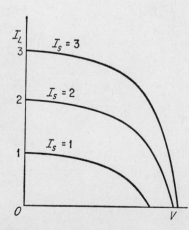

Fig. 6–7. EFFECT OF LIGHT INTENSITY ON THE LOAD CURRENT VERSUS TERMINAL VOLTAGE CURVE.

Equation (6–8) can be represented by the equivalent circuit of Fig. 6–6(b). A photovoltaic cell behaves very much like a current generator connected in parallel to a diode which is connected unfortunately in a direction allowing the bypass of the photon-generated current.

It is readily seen from Eq. (6–8) that the load current versus load voltage characteristics is simply the upsidedown curve of Fig. 6–2 raised in the vertical direction by an amount I_s. This is plotted in Fig. 6–7 with different values of I_s. For light beams of the same color, I_s is directly proportional to the intensity of light. The significant points of the $I_L - V$ characteristics are as follows:

1. *Open-circuit Voltage,* V_0

With $I_L = 0$, Eq. (6–8) gives

$$I_s = I_0(e^{eV_0/kT} - 1)$$

$$V_0 = V_T \log\left(\frac{I_s}{I_0} + 1\right) \tag{6–9}$$

where V_T is the thermal voltage kT/e.

For the same T, V_0 increases logarithmically with I_s and I_s increases proportionately with light intensity. These relations for a typical solar cell are plotted in Fig. 6–8.

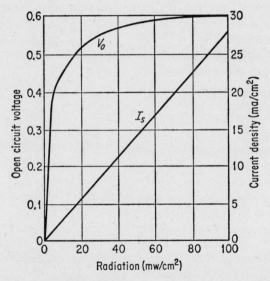

Fig. 6–8. OPEN-CIRCUIT VOLTAGE AND SHORT CIRCUIT CURRENT AS FUNCTIONS OF LIGHT INTENSITY. (Reprinted from P. Rappaport, "The Photovoltaic Effect and Its Utilization" *RCA Review*, Vol. **20**, No. 3, September 1959, pp. 373–397.)

2. *Maximum Efficiency and Maximum Output*

Because the input power is in the form of a beam of light and is independent of the output condition, the operating point of maximum output is also that of maximum efficiency. For each load voltage V, the load current is given by Eq. (6–8). The output power can be expressed as a function of V:

$$P = V[I_s - I_0(e^{V/V_T} - 1)] \tag{6–10}$$

Differentiating P with respect to V and setting the result to zero gives

$$0 = I_s - I_0(e^{V/V_T} - 1) - \frac{VI_0}{V_T} e^{V/V_T}$$

$$\left(\frac{I_s}{I_0} + 1\right) = e^{V/V_T}\left(1 + \frac{V}{V_T}\right) \tag{6-11}$$

Equation (6–11) gives V at maximum output as a function of I_s/I_0. From Eq. (6–8) and Eq. (6–10), the current and maximum power output can also be calculated. Figure (6–9) gives the three dimensionless ratios V_m/V_0, I_m/I_s, and $P_m/V_0 I_s$ for various values of I_s/I_0, where V_m, I_m, and P_m are the voltage, current, and power delivered to the load at the operating point for maximum P_m. We note that the curved $I_L - V$ characteristic is indeed advantageous from the point of view of power utilization. If I_L decreases linearly with V, then the three ratios at maximum output are simply 0.5, 0.5, and 0.25. Thus, for the same open-circuit voltage V_0 and short-circuit current I_s, the curved characteristics of Fig. 6–7 give two to three times as much output as that of the linear case.

3. *Efficiency versus Light Intensity*

The efficiency of a photovoltaic cell increases with the intensity of the light beam. Assuming that the Fourier composition or color of the light beam remains unchanged, the input power and I_s are proportional to the light intensity, whereas V_0, $P_m/V_0 I_s$ increase with light intensity.

A limit to the improvement in efficiency is reached when the terminal voltage V_m is still less than, but almost equal to, E_1 of Fig. 6–1. This is so because Eq. (6–8) is valid only if some potential gradient in the right direction is maintained at the junction.

Example 6–2: Assuming that the relative response (Fig. 6–5) is at its maximum when the wavelength of the light beam is 75% of the cutoff wavelength of the crystal, determine the wavelengths of maximum response for Ga As ($E_g = 1.34$ volts) and Cd Te ($E_g = 1.45$ volts).

SOLUTION: Let λ_m denote the wavelength of maximum response.

For Ga As

$$\lambda_m = \frac{12398}{1.34} \times 0.75 = 6930 \text{ Å}$$

For Cd Te

$$\lambda_m = \frac{12398}{1.45} \times 0.75 = 6410 \text{ Å}$$

Example 6-3: The maximum reversed current I_0 of a certain silicon cell is 0.01 microampere. Its short-circuit current I_s when exposed to sunlight is 5 amp. The operating temperature is 25°C. Calculate the following:

  (a) Open-circuit voltage
  (b) Maximum output
  (c) Load current and voltage for maximum output

SOLUTION:

$$V_T = 8.616 \times 10^{-5} \times 298 = 0.0257$$

$$V_0 = V_T \log\left(1 + \frac{5}{10^{-8}}\right) = V_T \frac{8.7}{0.434}$$

$$= 0.0257 \times 20 = 0.52 \text{ volt}$$

From Fig. 6–9, the following readings are obtained for a I_s/I_0 value of 5×10^8:

$$\frac{V}{V_0} = 0.855 \qquad \frac{P}{V_0 I_s} = 0.808$$

$$\frac{I_L}{I_s} = 0.945$$

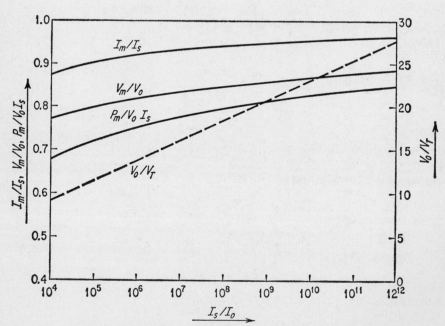

Fig. 6–9. MAXIMUM OUTPUT AND THE OPERATING POINT FOR MAXIMUM OUTPUT.

Therefore, for the maximum output point,

$$V = 0.52 \times 0.855 = 0.445$$

$$I_L = 5 \times 0.945 = 4.72$$

$$P = 0.445 \times 4.72 = 2.1 \text{ watt}$$

6-5. CONVERSION EFFICIENCY

The conversion efficiency is defined as

$$\eta = \frac{VI}{NeE_{ph}} \tag{6-12}$$

where VI is the output electric power, E_{ph} is the average photon energy in electron volts, and N is the number of incident photons per second. The product NeE_{ph} is the power of the incident light beam. Let

$K_1 =$ the fraction of photons which have succeeded in passing through the crystal surface.

$K_2 =$ the fraction of photons which have succeeded in freeing a valence electron sufficiently close to the junction to cause a minority carrier to go over the junction.

Then,

$$I_s = eNK_1K_2$$

and Eq. (6–12) can be written as

$$\eta = K_1K_2 \frac{VI}{E_{ph}I_s} \tag{6-13}$$

For maximum conversion efficiency, η_m, V, and I in Eq. (6–13) are replaced by V_m and I_m respectively. Because $I_s \gg I_0$, and exp $\{V_m/V_T\} \gg 1$, Eq. (6–11) and Eq. (6–8) become

$$\frac{I_s}{I_0} = e^{V_m/V_T}\left(1 + \frac{V_m}{V_T}\right) \tag{6-14}$$

$$\frac{I_m}{I_s} = 1 - \frac{I_0}{I_s}e^{V_m/V_T} = 1 - \frac{1}{1 + V_m/V_T} = \frac{V_m}{V_m + V_T} \tag{6-15}$$

Substituting Eq. (6–15) into Eq. (6–13) gives

$$\eta_m = K_1K_2\left(\frac{V_m}{V_m + V_T} \cdot \frac{V_m}{E_{ph}}\right) \tag{6-16}$$

Equation (6–15) shows that the maximum conversion efficiency is a product of four ratios, each of which is less than unity. The two ratios K_1 and $V_m/(V_m + V_T)$ are quite close to unity: $K_1 \cong 0.95$; $V_m/(V_m + V_T) \cong 0.95$. Assuming these values, Eq. (6–16) becomes

$$\eta_m = 0.9 \ K_2 \left(\frac{V_m}{E_{ph}} \right) \tag{6–17}$$

From Eq. (6–17), the maximum theoretical efficiency can be estimated: Using monochromatic light with E_{ph} slightly larger than E_g so that maximum response is obtained, K_2 and V_m can be as high as 0.9 and 0.75 E_{ph} respectively. The estimated maximum efficiency is then about 60%. With silicon cells energized by sunlight, K_2 is about 2/3, and V_m is about $E_{ph}/3$. The estimated maximum efficiency is about 20%. Test results for silicon cells range from 7% to 14% when these cells are energized by sunlight.

When different materials are used in a solar cell, K_2 reduces with increasing gap energy but V_m increases with increasing gap energy. A compromise between these two effects must be made.

Another relevant factor is the change of performance with temperature. The efficiency of a photovoltaic cell decreases as temperature increases. Referring to Sec. 3–11, the Fermi levels of doped semiconductors shift toward the center of the forbidden band as temperature increases. Consequently, E_1 of Fig. 6–1 is decreased and the available output voltage is also decreased. Furthermore, as I_0 increases with temperature exponentially and I_s is practically independent of temperature, the ratio I_s/I_0 is decreased with increased temperature. All these effects cause $P/V_0 I_s$ to decrease when temperature is increased.

Figure 6–10 illustrates the calculated efficiency of a solar cell versus its energy gap for various temperatures. It is to be noted that the optimum semiconductor energy gap increases as the temperature is increased. Thus at room temperature, cadmium telluride is the optimum material, whereas at 300°C the optimum is material "Z" with an energy gap of 1.8 electron volts. The material "Y" gives best over-all performance for the temperature range from room temperature to 300°C. It is generally possible to modify the energy gap by using ternary compounds, and the materials "Y" and "Z" could very well be made in that way. To quote Rappaport:*

The major problems encountered in making efficient solar converters from these new materials were

(1) Making suitable ohmic contact to the n and p regions. Rectifying or high-resistance contacts lower the output voltage and current appreciably. In general,

---

* Reprinted from P. Rappaport, "The Photovoltaic Effect and Its Utilization" *RCA Rev.* **20.** No. 3, (September, 1959) pp. 373–397.

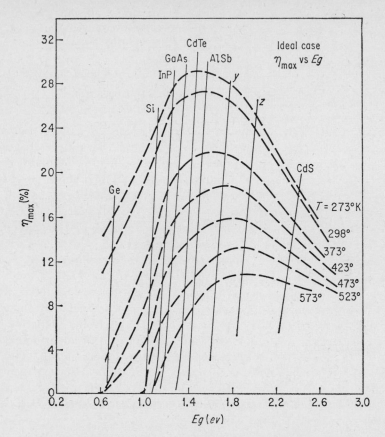

Fig. 6-10. Efficiency versus Energy Gap for Various Temperatures. (Reprinted from P. Rappaport, "The Photovoltaic Effect and Its Utilization" *RCA Review*, Vol. **20**, No. 3, September 1959, pp. 373–397.)

metallic plating and soldering, or an indium alloy dot solves the problem. Figure 6–11 shows the difference in current-voltage characteristics caused by poor contacts in Ga As.

(2) The need for low resistivity in the *p*- and *n*-type regions. This is required to obtain the maximum voltage per junction and a low series resistance. This problem is solved by using highly doped original material and by controlling the alloy or diffusion process to get a maximum impurity concentration.

(3) The fact that the *p-n* junctions do not behave according to theory. This can be caused by crystal imperfections, current leakage across the junction, or poor ohmic contact. The solution to this problem lies in better material, proper etching, lower diffusion temperature, and improved ohmic contacts.

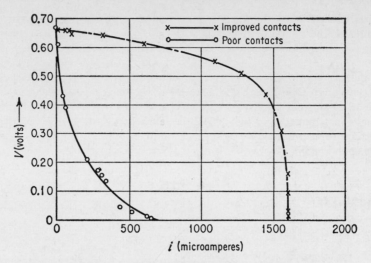

Fig. 6–11. Effect of Contacts on Current-voltage Characteristics of Ga-As Solar Cell. (Reprinted from P. Rappaport, "The Photovoltaic Effect and Its Utilization" *RCA Review*, Vol. **20**, No. 3, September 1959, pp. 373–397.)

6-6. CONCLUSION

For conclusion, we shall quote Rappaport again:*

The advantages of present solar cells as energy conversion devices are:

(1) Photovoltaic cells have given the highest over-all conversion efficiency from sunlight to electricity yet measured. The best value reported is 14 per cent.

(2) Such cells are easy to fabricate, being one of the simplest of semiconductor devices.

(3) They have unlimited life.

(4) They have high power-to-weight ratio for satellite applications. Cells having an efficiency of 10 per cent yield 50 watts per pound on the ground in sunlight of 100 mw/cm² , and about 12.5 watts per pound on a satellite in sunlight of 135 mw/cm² where tumbling, rotation, cell matching, higher temperature, light losses in cover, and other factors are taken into account. A cell 15 mils thick with contacts is considered in the above.

(5) Photovoltaic cells are area devices that don't require high temperatures for high efficiencies, thus eliminating lenses and concentrators in all but very special applications.

---

* Reprinted from P. Rappaport, "The Photovoltaic Effect and Its Utilization" *RCA Rev.*, **20**. No. 3, (September, 1959) pp. 373–397.

(6) In large-scale application, the problems of power distribution by wires could be eliminated by the use of solar cells at the site where the power is required.

The two main disadvantages to date are the high cost and the need for a storage device.

In the near future, silicon solar cells should be available with efficiencies in the 15 per cent range. Cells using other materials or combination of materials should be capable of 20 per cent conversion efficiency, and large-area polycrystalline films in the square-foot range might yield 5 per cent efficiency. Such devices will represent very strong competition in the solar-energy-conversion field for the new thermo-electric or thermionic devices which are showing promise.

REFERENCES

1. Rappaport, P., "The Photovoltaic Effect and Its Utilization," *RCA Rev.,* **20,** No. 3 (September, 1959) pp. 373–97.

2. Shockley, W., *Electrons and Holes in Semiconductors,* p. 314. Princeton, N. J.: Van Nostrand, 1950.

3. Lehovec, K., "The Photo-Voltaic Effect," *Phys. Rev.,* **74,** August, 1948.

4. Loferski, J. J., "Theoretical Considerations Governing the Choice of the Optimum Semiconductor for Photovoltaic Solar Energy Conversion," *Jour. Applied Physics,* **27,** July, 1956.

5. Tallent, R. J., and Henry Oman, "Solar Cell Performance with Concentrated Sunlight," *AIEE Transactions,* **81.** Part II, *Application and Industry,* March, 1962, pp. 30–33.

6. Sproull, R. L., *Modern Physics,* pp. 74–81. New York: John Wiley & Sons, 1956.

7. Van Name, Jr., F. W., *Modern Physics,* pp. 30–35; 40–45. Englewood Cliffs, N. J.: Prentice-Hall, Inc., 1962.

PROBLEMS

6-1. Calculate the photon flux for a plane electromagnetic wave at 1 megacycle. The power of the electromagnetic wave is 1 micromicro watt per square meter.

6-2. The energy distribution of a certain light source is given by

$$dW = K\nu^3 e^{-\nu/\nu_0}\, d\nu$$

where dW is the intensity of the light beam with frequencies in the range $d\nu$ in watt/m², and K and ν_0 are constants. Assume that a crystal with energy gap E_g is used, and each photon with $h\nu \geq E_g$ causes a unit charge to cross the junction and each photon with $h\nu < E_g$ causes no conversion current at all. At what value of E_g is $E_g I_s$ a maximum? What percentage of photons have caused conversion current at this optimum value of E_g?

6-3. Discuss the effects of the following changes on the efficiency of a solar cell:
  (a) An increase in the coefficient of reflection at the crystal surface
  (b) An increase in reversed current
  (c) An increase in the diffusion lengths of minority carriers
  (d) An increase in the concentrations of majority carriers
  (e) An increase in the concentrations of minority carriers

6-4. The silicon solar cell of Ex. 6–3 is used under different conditions of light intensity, and I_s varies from 0.5 to 5 amp.

  (a) Plot the V versus I characteristic curves for $I_s = 0.5, 1, 2,$ and 5 amp respectively.
  (b) Assume that there is a series resistance of 0.1 ohm and replot the foregoing characteristics.

6-5. Repeat Prob. 6–4(a) and (b) with I_s kept constant at 5 amp but I_0 taking on various values: 0.01, 0.1, and 1 μa.

6-6. Assume that sunlight has an average intensity of 500 w/m² during an eight-hour period each day, and 15 days per month are rainy or cloudy. Estimate the total area of solar conversion needed to supply an average family with electricity at the rate of 500 kwh per month. Assume the efficiency of the solar cells to be 5%.

CHAPTER SEVEN

FREE ENERGY AND FUEL CELLS

Fuel cells convert chemical energy directly into electrical energy without going through the intermediary of heat and so eliminate a step which is always associated with marked increase in entropy. Fuel cells offer the possibility of more effective utilization of fossil fuel, theoretically estimated at doubling the output of the present steam turbine-generator unit with the same amount of fuel.

There are two kinds of technical problems: first, whether it is possible for a proposed process to take place; second, how to accelerate a theoretically possible process. The present chapter gives a thermodynamic solution to problems of the first kind, and a survey of current research efforts on problems of the second kind.

7-1. GENERAL DESCRIPTION OF AN ELECTROCHEMICAL PROCESS

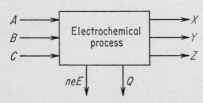

Fig. 7-1. BLOCK DIAGRAM OF AN ELECTROCHEMICAL PROCESS.

An electrochemical process can be described by the block diagram of Fig. 7-1. There are various substances A, B, C ... going into the process, and various substances X, Y, Z, coming out of the process. Those going into the process are called *reactants*; those coming out of the process are called *products*. Electrical energy neE may be generated or consumed by the process; heat Q may be liberated or absorbed; and mechanical work W may be done by the gas on the external system,

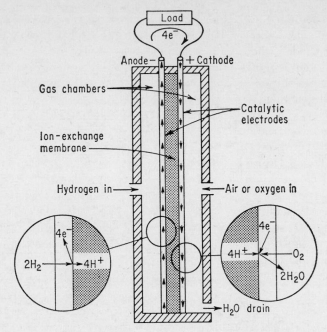

Fig. 7–2. A Fuel Cell of the Ion-exchange Membrane Type. (Reprinted from G. A. Phillips, "Status of the Ion-Exchange Membrane Fuel Cell" *Electrical Engineering*, Vol. **81**, No. 3, March 1962, pp. 194–201.)

or vice versa. As an example, consider the H_2-O_2 fuel cell illustrated in Fig. 7–2. Hydrogen and oxygen are supplied to the "anode" side and "cathode" side of the cell respectively. The two sides of the cell are divided by an ion-exchange membrane which allows the passage of hydrogen ions H^+ but not the oxygen O_2. The ion-exchange membrane is about 1 mm thick. Each surface of the membrane is coated with a catalyst that facilitates the cell reactions and also serves as the electrode. The reactions which take place can be expressed as

"Anode" reaction

$$2H_2 \longrightarrow 4H^+ + 4e \qquad (7\text{–}1)$$

"Cathode" reaction

$$4e + 4H^+ + O_2 \longrightarrow 2H_2O \qquad (7\text{–}2)$$

Over-all reaction

$$2H_2 + O_2 \longrightarrow 2H_2O + 4eE + Q - 3kT \qquad (7\text{–}3)$$

Equation (7–1) means that two hydrogen molecules become four hydrogen ions at the "anode" surface and four electrons are released. The electrons are then conducted away by the "anode" through the external load to the "cathode." The hydrogen ions pass through the ion-conducting membrane to the "cathode" where they recombine with O_2 and the electrons to form H_2O. This step is represented by Eq. (7-2). As the pressure of O_2 is above the vapor pressure of H_2O, the latter condenses and is drained away from the O_2 compartment.

The over-all reaction is summarized in (7-3): In addition to the chemical change, electrical energy $4eE$ and heat Q are released and mechanical energy $3RT$ is absorbed. The mechanical energy is present because the reactants H_2 and O_2 are in gaseous state but the product H_2O is in liquid state and occupies negligible volume. The hydrogen and oxygen sources are doing mechanical work when H_2 and O_2 are forced into the cell. For each mole of reaction Eq. (7-3), the work done by these sources are $2RT$ and RT respectively, where R is the universal constant and T is the temperature of the fuel cell. The work done by external sources per molecular reaction is $3RT/N_0 = 3kT$.

For the general case of Fig. 7-1, the over-all reaction can be written as

$$\sum_i n_i M_i \longrightarrow neE + Q + W \qquad (7\text{-}4)$$

where n_i is the number of molecules of type M_i entering into the reaction. The number n_i is positive if M_i is a reactant and is negative if M_i is a product. The mechanical work done by the reaction is denoted as W. Taking the H_2-O_2 fuel cell as an example, M_1, M_2, and M_3 represent H_2, O_2, and H_2O respectively; $n_1 = 2$, $n_2 = 1$, $n_3 = -2$, $n = 4$, and $W = -3kT$.

Equation (7-4) can also be interpreted on a macroscopic scale: There are n_i moles of substance M_i involved in each mole of reaction, e is the charge per mole of electrons (96,500 coulombs) and Q and W are the heat released and mechanical work done, respectively, per mole of reaction.

7-2. GIBBS FREE ENERGY

Let U_i represent the internal energy per molecule or per mole of M_i. Conservation of energy requires that

$$\sum_i n_i U_i = neE + Q + W \qquad (7\text{-}5)$$

Given any operating condition, which usually consists of the operating temperature and pressure or partial pressures of the gases, W per mole of reaction is completely fixed. Its value is given by

$$W = \sum_i p_i \Delta V_i \qquad (7\text{-}6)$$

where ΔV_i is the increase in volume of the substance M_i for each mole of reaction. Obviously ΔV_i is negative for the reactants and positive for the products. Let V_i denote the volume occupied by 1 mole of M_i under the operating condition (T, p_i). Then $\Delta V_i = -n_i V_i$, and Eq. (7–6) becomes

$$W = -\sum_i n_i p_i V_i \qquad (7\text{–}7)$$

Equation (7–5) shows that the excess energy of the reaction $\sum_i n_i U_i - W$ is either dissipated as heat or is converted to electrical energy. But it gives no indication of the partition between the two which is of greatest practical importance. Of course, we should like to have all the excess energy converted into neE, and, if possible, to make Q negative so that neE can be even larger. The limit is set, however, by the second law of thermodynamics.

Let S_i denote the entropy per mole of substance M_i under the operating condition: temperature T and pressure p_i. Consider the change in entropy of the entire system, including the chemical process and the environment with which it exchanges thermal energy. Since n_i moles of M_i disappear for each mole of reaction, its entropy disappears with it. The increase in entropy due to the change in chemical substances is

$$(\Delta S)_1 = -\sum_i n_i S_i \qquad (7\text{–}8)$$

Note that, as some n_i are negative, $(\Delta S)_1$ can be positive as well as negative. The increase in entropy of the environment is

$$(\Delta S)_2 = \frac{Q}{T} \qquad (7\text{–}9)$$

Since the delivery of electric energy neE and mechanical energy W does not involve any change in entropy, the total increase in entropy is

$$\Delta S = (\Delta S)_1 + (\Delta S)_2 = -\sum_i n_i S_i + \frac{Q}{T} \geq 0 \qquad (7\text{–}10)$$

The last inequality sign is due to the second law.

Inequality (7–10) can be written as

$$-T \sum_i n_i S_i + Q \geq 0 \qquad (7\text{–}11)$$

Substituting Eq. (7–5) and Eq. (7–7) into expression (7–11) gives

$$-T \sum_i n_i S_i + \sum_i n_i U_i + \sum_i n_i p_i V_i - neE \geq 0$$

The preceding inequality can be rewritten as

$$neE \leq \sum_i n_i(U_i + p_iV_i - TS_i) \qquad (7\text{-}12)$$

If the process is reversible, the equality sign holds in Eq. (7-10) and consequently also in Eq. (7-12).

The expression $U_i + p_iV_i - TS_i$ has a very important physical significance. Let it be denoted F_i. First, F_i has the dimension of energy. Second, $\sum_i n_iF_i$ represents a decrease of total F because of the reaction, and Eq. (7-12) means that this decrease in total F is equal to the electrical energy generated in a reversible process. As electrical energy does not have any entropy associated with it, it can be converted into any other form of energy. Thus the energy $\sum_i n_iF_i$ is also free to be converted into any other form of energy.

In Sec. 2-3, we discussed the significance of orderly and disorderly forms of energy. Electrical and mechanical energies are orderly forms of energy, whereas thermal energy is a disorderly form of energy. Chemical energy is a mixture of both. Later, in Chapter 2, we introduced the notion of entropy and showed that entropy is associated only with the disorderly thermal energy and that the orderly forms of energies do not have any entropy associated with them. The discussion in this chapter allows the excess energy released in a chemical reaction, $\sum_i n_iU_i - W$, to be separated precisely into two parts: an entropy-free part $\sum_i n_iF_i$ and a thermal energy Q.

A more perceptive way of comprehending the foregoing is to regard U_i as consisting of two parts: an entropy-free part F_i, and a remaining part in thermal energy. The sum $\sum_i n_iF_i$ represents the excess in entropy-free energy of the reactants over that of the products. It is, therefore, the entropy-free energy released in the reaction and can be converted into other forms of entropy-free energy.

Dropping the subscript i, the entropy-free energy of a substance is

$$F = U + pV - TS \qquad (7\text{-}13)$$

F is called *Gibbs free energy* or *Lewis's free energy* in honor of the pioneer investigators who have discovered its significance. Another reason for naming F after a person is distinguishing it from the other forms of free energies in thermodynamics which will be discussed in a later section.

Equation (7-12) can now be written as

$$neE \leq \sum_i n_iF_i \qquad (7\text{-}14)$$

$$E \leq \frac{1}{ne} \sum_i n_iF_i \qquad (7\text{-}15)$$

Equation (7–15) sets a limit to the generated emf of an electrochemical process in terms of the free energies of the reactants and products. The equality sign is to hold for reversible processes. For many basically reversible reactions, however, the experimentally measured E is less than its theoretical value, if the reaction generates electricity, and is greater than its theoretical value if the reaction consumes electricity. The reason for this discrepancy is not completely known. It may be caused by the following two effects among others:

(1) Catalysts are generally used at the electrodes to speed up the reaction. As the reactions with the catalysts are usually not reversible, they cause the entropy to rise and E to decrease accordingly.

(2) The concentrations of the ions at the electrodes are generally lower than their equilibrium value with the un-ionized gas for various reasons. For instance, in the H_2-O_2 fuel cell described in Sec. 7–1, the H^+ ion concentration at the "cathode" is limited by various effects which will be discussed later. Although the H^+ ion concentration at the "anode" is approximately in equilibrium with the H_2 pressure, its value at the "cathode" is considerably lower and is not in equilibrium with the latter.

The total energy released in a reaction can be expressed in terms of the heat content H:

$$H = U + pV \qquad (7\text{–}16)$$

(See Sec. 5–6a for the enthalpy flux.) Equations (7–5) and (7–7) give

$$neE + Q = \sum_i n_i(U_i + p_iV_i) = \sum_i n_iH_i \qquad (7\text{–}17)$$

Equations (7–14) and (7–17) give

$$Q \geq \sum_i n_i(H_i - F_i) \qquad (7\text{–}18)$$

The total energy released in a chemical reaction is $\sum_i n_iH_i$. Its distribution is restricted by inequalities (7–14) and (7–18).

Example 7–1: The change in heat content, and Gibbs' free energy for the reaction $2H_2 + O_2 \rightarrow 2H_2O$ are given as

$$\Delta H = -\sum_i n_i H_i = -136.5 \text{ kcal/mole}$$

$$\Delta F = -\sum_i n_i F_i = -113.4 \text{ kcal/mole}$$

where H_2 and O_2 are gases at 25°C and 1 atm, and H_2O is in liquid state. Calculate the theoretical values of the emf generated in a H_2-O_2 fuel cell and the heat released.

SOLUTION: There are 4e generated in each molecular reaction. Therefore, the maximum emf generated is

$$E \leq \frac{113.4 \times 4.18}{96.5 \times 4} = 1.23 \text{ volts}$$

The heat released is at least $136.5 - 113.4 = 23.1$ kcal per mole.

7-3. CHANGE OF FREE ENERGY WITH TEMPERATURE AND PRESSURE

In the expression for free energy,

$$F = U + pV - TS = H - TS \tag{7-19}$$

p, V, and T are readily measurable quantities, but U, H, and S are not. Theoretically the values of U, H, and S are zero at $0°K$, and their values at other temperatures can be obtained by integration. This, however, is impractical to do. Not only are measurements near $0°K$ difficult to make, most materials behave abnormally at these low temperatures and it is impossible to extrapolate.

The only recourse then is the direct measurement of ΔF for a given reaction at some standard condition from the reaction itself. The ΔF at other conditions are then calculated from ΔF at the standard condition.

To illustrate this procedure, let us assume that, in the temperatures and pressures of interest, the following conditions are valid:

(1) The reactants and products are either ideal gases or liquids or solids. The ones which are liquids or solids occupy negligible volume.

(2) The specific heats at constant pressure are constants.
For an ideal gas,

$$\Delta H = \Delta U + \Delta(pV)$$

$$= C_V \Delta T + \Delta(RT) = (C_V + R) \Delta T$$

$$= C_p \Delta T \tag{7-20}$$

Note that Eq. (7-20) is valid whether the pressure varies or not. For a solid or a liquid, pV is negligible, C_p and C_V are the same and Eq. (7-20) is also true.

Let the superscript ^{o} be used to denote the thermodynamic variables at the standard condition. Equation (7-20) can be written as

$$H - H^o = C_p(T - T^o) \tag{7-21}$$

The change in entropy will now be calculated:

$$T\,dS = dU + p\,dV = d(U + pV) - V\,dp = dH - V\,dp = C_p\,dT - V\,dp$$

$$(7\text{–}22)$$

For gas

$$dS = C_p \frac{dT}{T} - R \frac{dp}{p}$$

$$S - S^o = C_p \log \frac{T}{T^o} - R \log \frac{p}{p^o} \tag{7–23}$$

For liquids and solids

$$dS = C_p \frac{dT}{T}$$

$$S - S^o = C_p \log \frac{T}{T^o} \tag{7–24}$$

From Eq. (7–23) and Eq. (7–24), the change in TS is calculated:

$$TS - T^o S^o = C_p T \log \frac{T}{T^o} - \left[RT \log \frac{p}{p^o} \right]_g + S^o(T - T^o) \quad (7\text{–}25)$$

where $[\;\;]_g$ means that the term inside is there for gases only. From Eq. (7–21) and Eq. (7–25), we obtain

$$F - F^o = (C_p - S^o)(T - T^o) - C_p T \log \frac{T}{T^o} + \left[RT \log \frac{p}{p^o} \right]_g \quad (7\text{–}26)$$

Summing Eq. (7–26) over all reactants and products, we obtain finally

$$\sum_i n_i F_i - \sum_i n_i F_i^o = \left[\sum_i n_i C_{p_i} - \sum_i n_i S_i^o \right](T - T^o)$$

$$- \left(\sum_i n_i C_{p_i} \right) T \log \frac{T}{T^o} + RT \sum_i{}' n_i \log \frac{p_i}{p_i^o} \quad (7\text{–}27)$$

In Eq. (7–27), $\sum{}'$ means that only the gases are included in the sum. We note that the only unmeasurable quantity on the right-hand side of Eq. (7–27) is S_i^o. The sum $\sum_i n_i S_i^o$ can, however, be calculated as

$$\sum_i n_i S_i^o = \frac{1}{T^o} \left(\sum_i n_i H_i^o - \sum_i n_i F_i^o \right) \tag{7–28}$$

Example 7–2: If the pressures of H_2 and O_2 are increased equally without changing the temperature of the fuel cell in Ex. 7–1, at what pressure is it possible to convert the excess energy of the reaction entirely into electrical energy at least theoretically?

SOLUTION: Since H does not change with pressure under the assumptions stated, it is necessary to increase the excess free energy to the same value as the heat released. Therefore,

$$\sum_i n_i F_i - \sum_i n_i F_i^o = 136.5 - 113.4 = 23.1 \text{ kcal per mole}$$

Equation (7–27) gives

$$23.1 = 3RT \log \frac{p}{p^o}$$

$$\frac{p}{p^o} = \exp\left(\frac{23.1 \times 10^3}{3 \times 1.987 \times 298}\right) = e^{13} = 5000$$

The pressures of O_2 and H_2 have to be increased to 5000 atm.

7-4. THE GIBBS-HELMHOLTZ EQUATION

The Gibbs-Helmholtz equation gives the exact temperature coefficient of the electromotive force in a reversible electrochemical process. Unlike Eq. (7–28), its validity is universal and is not limited to processes involving only materials with idealized or approximately idealized properties.

From Eq. (7–19), the total differential of the free energy F of any given substance is

$$dF = dU + p\,dV + V\,dp - T\,dS - S\,dT$$

$$= V\,dp - S\,dT \tag{7–29}$$

According to Sec. 2–2, T and p can be selected as the two independent variables specifying the state of the substance. As F is a variable of the state, it can be expressed as a function of the two variables T and p. Therefore,

$$dF = \left(\frac{\partial F}{\partial p}\right)_T dp + \left(\frac{\partial F}{\partial T}\right)_p dT \tag{7–30}$$

where the subscripts T and p mean that in taking the partial derivative of F with respect to one variable, the other variable is kept constant. Comparing Eq. (7–29) and Eq. (7–30) gives

$$\left(\frac{\partial F}{\partial T}\right)_p = -S \qquad (7\text{--}31)$$

For a reversible electrochemical process, the equality sign of Eq. (7–15) holds

$$neE = \sum_i n_i F_i \qquad (7\text{--}32)$$

Differentiating Eq. (7–32) with respect to T while keeping all the pressures p_i constant gives

$$ne\left(\frac{\partial E}{\partial T}\right)_p = \sum_i n_i \left(\frac{\partial F_i}{\partial T}\right)_{p_i} = -\sum_i n_i S_i \qquad (7\text{--}33)$$

The last equality sign is due to Eq. (7–31). Multiplying Eq. (7–33) by T and substituting $H_i - F_i$ for TS_i gives

$$neT\left(\frac{\partial E}{\partial T}\right)_p = \sum_i n_i F_i - \sum_i n_i H_i$$

$$= neE - \sum_i n_i H_i$$

The preceding equation can be rewritten as

$$E - T\left(\frac{\partial E}{\partial T}\right)_p = \frac{1}{ne}\sum_i n_i H_i \equiv E_h \qquad (7\text{--}34)$$

where E_h would be the emf if all the energy liberated from the reaction were converted into electrical energy. Equation (7–34) is known as the *Gibbs-Helmholtz equation*.

An interesting conclusion from Eq. (7–34) is that the temperature coefficient of the emf is negative in a reversible process in which the converted electrical energy is less than the total energy liberated from the process.

We can carry the above derivation one step further to find an expression for $\partial^2 E / \partial T^2$. Since

$$T\,dS = dU + p\,dV = dH - V\,dp$$

$$= \left(\frac{\partial H}{\partial T}\right)_p dT + \left[\left(\frac{\partial H}{\partial p}\right)_T - V\right] dp$$

$$= C_p\,dT + \left[\left(\frac{\partial H}{\partial p}\right)_T - V\right] dp \qquad (7\text{--}35)$$

As S is a variable of the state, it can be expressed as a function of p and T. Therefore,

$$dS = \left(\frac{\partial S}{\partial T}\right)_p dT + \left(\frac{\partial S}{\partial p}\right)_T dp \qquad (7\text{–}36)$$

Comparing Eq. (7–35) with Eq. (7–36) gives

$$\left(\frac{dS}{dT}\right)_p = \frac{C_p}{T} \qquad (7\text{–}37)$$

Differentiating Eq. (7–33) with respect to T gives

$$ne\left(\frac{\partial^2 E}{\partial T^2}\right)_p = -\sum_i n_i \left(\frac{\partial S_i}{\partial T}\right)_{p_i} = -\frac{1}{T}\sum_i n_i C_{pi} \qquad (7\text{–}38)$$

Example 7–3: Calculate the temperature coefficient of the emf for the fuel cell of Ex. 7–1, assuming that it is a reversible process.

SOLUTION: By definition,

$$E_h = \frac{136.5 \times 4.18}{96.5 \times 4} = 1.48 \text{ volts}$$

Equation (7–34) gives

$$\left(\frac{\partial E}{\partial T}\right)_p = -\frac{E_h - E}{T} = -\frac{1.48 - 1.23}{273 + 25} = -0.84 \times 10^{-3} \text{ volt/degrees K}$$

7-5. PROCESSES WITH CHANGING TEMPERATURE AND PRESSURE

In the preceding derivation of the relation between the emf of an electrochemical process and Gibbs free energy, the only important assumption is that of uniform temperature for all the reactants and products in the process. It is not necessary to assume that the temperature and pressures remain constant. For a process with changing temperature and pressures, one may consider a very small change Δ at a time, say, one-millionth of a mole. Only the small fractions of reactants which take part in the very small change Δ and products which are direct yields from Δ are considered parts of the system. The bulk of the reactants and products which are already there are considered parts of the environment. Within the process Δ, p_i and T can be regarded as constants, and consequently Eq. (7–12) and Eq. (7–15) are still valid. As a process with varying p_i and T can be broken up into a succession of processes Δ, these equations are expected to hold at every stage. Thus we come to the following conclusion:

In a process with varying p_i and T, Eq. (7-12) and Eq. (7-15) hold at every instant. The equality signs in these equations apply if the process is reversible.

The only assumption then is that of uniform temperature throughout the process. Even this assumption is not as restrictive as it sounds, however, if only an approximate result is of interest. For instance, if there is a temperature difference of 100°C between the reactants H_2 and O_2 of Ex. 7-1. The change in energy released should not be greater than what is required to heat or to cool one of the gases by 100°C. As O_2 has a specific heat per molecule of $7k/2$,

$$\tfrac{7}{2}k\,\Delta T = \tfrac{7}{2} \times 8.616 \times 10^{-5} \text{ ev/deg} \times 100 \text{ deg} = 0.03 \text{ ev}$$

The theoretical energy released per molecule of O_2 is $1.23 \times 4 = 4.92$ ev. Thus, the error due to a temperature difference of 100°C is only about 1%.

7-6. THERMODYNAMIC FREE ENERGIES AND CONDITIONS OF EQUILIBRIUM

The treatment of Gibbs free energy in the preceding sections is quite adequate for all practical purposes concerning a fuel cell. As the subject of free energies is of considerable importance, however, it is worthwhile to treat the subject once again from a more general standpoint.

Consider a system of uniform temperature T having a flexible exterior wall which permits free heat exchange. The system is compartmentized with volumes V_i. Correspondingly, pressures p_i are exerted by the system on various parts of the exterior wall. The total entropy and internal energy of the system are denoted as S and U. For a certain process, the increments in S, U, p_i and V_i are ΔS, ΔU, Δp_i, and ΔV_i respectively. Assuming that the process can take place only slightly, these are infinitesimal or minute increments. In addition to the mechanical work $\sum_i p_i \, \Delta V_i$ done by the system on its environment, the process also delivers some other form of entropy-free energy ΔW (e.g., electrical energy neE).

Let ΔQ represent the heat absorbed by the system from its environment. The conservation of energy requires that

$$\Delta Q = \Delta U + \sum_i p_i \, \Delta V_i + \Delta W \tag{7-39}$$

As the entropy of the environment is reduced by $\Delta Q/T$, the second law of thermodynamics requires that

$$\Delta S - \frac{\Delta Q}{T} \geq 0 \tag{7–40}$$

It is obtained from Eq. (7–39) and Eq. (7–40)

$$\Delta W \leq T \Delta S - \Delta U - \sum_i p_i \Delta V_i \tag{7–41}$$

For a reversible process, the equality sign of Eq. (7–41) holds, and ΔW has the following significances:

(1) If $\Delta W > 0$, the process can take place spontaneously. An entropy-free output energy of at most ΔW can be obtained from the process.

(2) If $\Delta W < 0$, the process cannot take place spontaneously. In order to make it happen, an external, entropy-free energy of at least ΔW must be supplied to the process.

(3) The relation $\Delta W = 0$ gives the condition of equilibrium. A system with $\Delta W = 0$ is in a state of equilibrium insofar as the particular process is concerned.

Under certain external conditions, the expression on the right-hand side of Eq. (7–41) can be written as a decrease of some appropriate variable of the state. The latter is then called a *free energy* of the system. Its significance is that an entropy-free output can be obtained only as a decrease in the free energy of the system:

$$\Delta W = -\Delta F \tag{7–42}$$

A list of the external conditions and the corresponding free energy function is given in Table 7–1.

TABLE 7–1

External Condition	Free Energy	Condition for Process to Take Place
Constant T and p_i	$H - TS$	$-\Delta(H - TS) \geq \Delta W$
Constant T and V_i	$U - TS$	$-\Delta(U - TS) \geq \Delta W$
Constant S and p_i	H	$-\Delta H \geq \Delta W$
Constant S and V_i	U	$-\Delta U \geq \Delta W$
Adiabatic process, $\Delta Q = 0$		$\Delta S \geq 0$

In Table 7–1, H is the enthalpy or heat content:

$$H = U + \sum_i p_i V_i$$

To show how the entries in Table 7–1 are obtained, let us consider the case of constant T and V_i. From the assumed condition,

$$\Delta V_i = 0$$

$$T \Delta S = \Delta(TS)$$

inequality (7–41) becomes

$$\Delta W \leq \Delta(TS - U) = -\Delta(U - TS)$$

The function $U - TS$ is called *Helmholtz free energy*.

For the case of constant S and p_i, $\Delta S = 0$, and $p_i \Delta V_i = \Delta(p_i V_i)$. Inequality (7–41) gives

$$\Delta W \leq -\Delta(U + \sum_i p_i V_i) = -\Delta H$$

A process with constant entropy is called an *isentropic* process. A process with $\Delta Q = 0$ is called an *adiabatic* process. The latter means that there is no exchange of heat between the system and its environment. If the process is reversible, then the equality sign of expression (7–40) must hold. An isentropic process is then adiabatic and vice versa. But the two are not the same in the general case. For an adiabatic process, expression (7–40) reduces to

$$\Delta S \geq 0$$

as a necessary condition for the process to occur. There is no function which determines both the condition of equilibrium and the amount of entropy-free energy to be gained from the process.

Table 7–1 gives the appropriate free energies under various external conditions as $H - TS$, $U - TS$, H, and U. Because H and U are already known as *enthalpy* and *internal energy* respectively, only $H - TS$ and $U - TS$ are called *free energies*. From the way each is derived, Gibbs free energy $H - TS$ is generally associated with constant-pressure processes and Helmholtz free energy $U - TS$ is generally associated with constant volume processes.

7-7. WHICH FREE ENERGY? A PUZZLE AND A SOLUTION

Some textbooks on thermodynamics argue that Gibbs free energy is used for determining the condition of equilibrium in chemical processes because these are constant-pressure processes. The argument is somewhat misleading: Many chemical processes take place inside a rigid enclosure and therefore the volume is constant instead of the pressure. Why then should not Helmholtz free energy be used instead of Gibbs free energy to determine the condition of equilibrium?

To be more specific, consider the electrochemical process described in Sec. 7–1 and Sec. 7–2: If a minute fraction, m, of a mole of the reaction takes place, each substance M_i is decreased by an amount $n_i m$. At first glance, the total decrease in Helmholtz free energy is

$$\Delta(U - TS) = - \sum_i n_i m(U_i - TS_i) \qquad (7\text{--}43)?$$

Should not expression (7–12) be replaced by

$$neE \leq \sum_i n_i(U_i - TS_i) \qquad (7\text{--}44)?$$

First, we shall attempt a common-sense answer. If expression (7–12) were true only for constant-pressure processes, and (7–44) were true for constant-volume processes, we could well imagine a chemical process which had reached equilibrium in a certain container under condition of constant pressure, and which was set into motion again by shutting off a valve at some remote place without ever disturbing the contents of the container, but thereby changing the process into a constant-volume process. If we were ingenious enough, we could probably set up a perpetual motion inside the container by turning the valve on and off and utilize the perpetual motion to get some work out of it. Of course, these things are not possible.

The fallacy does not lie in the use of Helmholtz free energy, but in calculating the change of Helmholtz free energy by Eq. (7–43). As the volume remains constant, the partial pressures of each substance are necessarily changed. Thus the change in Helmholtz free energy has two parts: One part is the free energy of the newly added or subtracted portion of each substance as given in Eq. (7–43). Another part is the change in Helmholtz free energy of the different substances which are already there. When both parts are taken into consideration, $\Delta(U - TS)$ *at constant volume is identical to* $\Delta(H - TS)$ *at constant pressure.*

To illustrate this point, consider a chemical process involving a mixture of ideal gases. A mixture of ideal gases is easy to calculate, as it has the following desirable properties:

(1) The functions U_i and S_i per mole of each gas depend on T, and T, p_i only, where p_i is the partial pressure, and are independent of the presence of the other gases.

In the foregoing special case, it has been proved that, owing to a change in m_i,

$$\Delta(H - TS)_{T,p} = \Delta(U - TS)_{T,V}$$

Thus the condition of equilibrium and the amount of entropy-free energy which can be obtained from the process (or which must be supplied to the process) per mole are independent of the external conditions but depend only on the instantaneous values of the temperature T and partial pressures p_i.

Actually a much more general result can be proved. For a chemical process involving not only ideal gases but any kind of substances, the following relations are valid:

$$(\Delta H)_{S,p} = (\Delta U)_{S,V} = \Delta(H - TS)_{T,p} = \Delta(U - TS)_{T,V}$$

Hence the real significance of Table 7-1 is not to give different values of ΔW under various external conditions, but to give different formulas for calculating the same ΔW. Gibbs free energy is the easiest to calculate because its value per mole remains constant if the temperature and pressures remain constant.

7-8. DEFINITION AND GENERAL DESCRIPTION OF A FUEL CELL

A *fuel cell* is an electrochemical device in which the chemical energy of a conventional fuel is converted directly into electrical energy. To start with we shall answer the two following questions:

1. Why do we want to do this?
2. What are the necessary features in such a device?

The first question can best be answered with the help of Fig. 7-3 and Fig. 7-4 in which the total energy released $-\Delta H = \sum_i n_i H_i$ and free energy released $-\Delta F = \sum_i n_i F_i$ are plotted against temperature for the oxidation of two basic fuel elements

$$2H_2 + O_2 \longrightarrow 2H_2O$$

$$C + O_2 \longrightarrow CO_2$$

At any given temperature, the entire heat of reaction $(-\Delta H)$ may be released as heat, or a very substantial part of $(-\Delta H)$ up to $(-\Delta F)$ can be converted into electrical energy by a fuel cell and the remaining part of $(-\Delta H)$ be released as heat In either case, the released heat can then be converted in part into electrical energy by heat engines of various types if

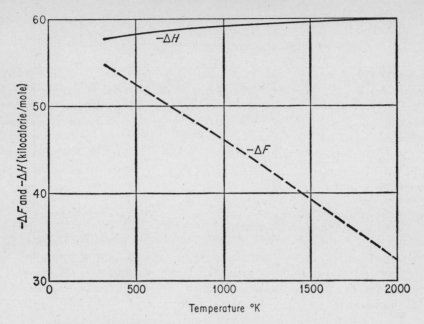

Fig. 7–3. The Enthalpy and Gibbs Free Energy Released by the Reaction $2 H_2 + O_2 \rightarrow 2 H_2O$

the temperature at which the reaction takes place is sufficiently high. The arrangements are illustrated in Fig. 7–5. The advantage of the latter scheme, Fig. 7–5(b), in terms of efficiency is quite obvious.

Because of the corrosion of electrodes at high temperature, there is some doubt whether a feasible fuel cell can ever be made to operate at modern boiler temperature. Figure 7–5(b) may not be realistic. If we compare a present-day heat engine with a fuel cell operating at low temperature, which usually converts 60% to 90% of $-\Delta F$ to electrical energy, the fuel cell is still the more efficient device.

Another but more immediate reason for the current interest in fuel cells is that their efficiency and weight and cost per kilowatt are independent of the power rating down to a few watts. This property makes the prospects of fuel cells very attractive as portable power plants in various applications: e.g., to provide electrical power for spacecraft, to replace the diesel electric generator in locomotives, etc. With further improvements in cost and durability, applications can readily be found in a wide range of commercial products. Even in its present stage of development, the fuel cell gives a few times more electrical energy or power per unit weight than a storage battery or a turbine generator set. Its efficiency is already high compared to existing portable power plants.

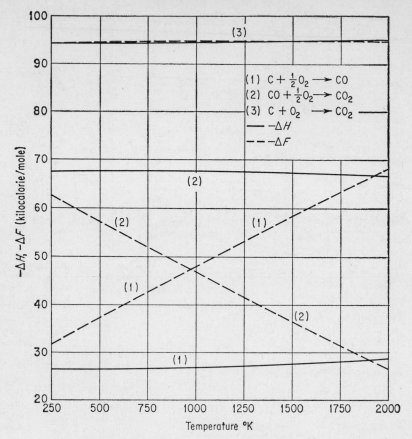

Fig. 7–4. THE ENTHALPY AND GIBBS FREE ENERGY RELEASED
BY THE REACTION $C + O_2 \rightarrow CO_2$.

To determine the necessary features in a fuel cell, we note that in
"burning" a fuel, the fuel atom loses one or more of its electrons to an
atom of oxygen, and the resulting ions are bound by electrostatic attraction.
In this process, some excess energy is released as heat. In a fuel cell, the
ions are forced to do some work before they are allowed to come together.
The situation is illustrated in Fig. 7–6, which is a rough sketch of the electric
potential inside a fuel cell. Either the negative ion travels from electrode B
to electrode A or the positive ion travels from electrode A to electrode B. In
either case, the traveling ions lose energy and also give the effect of an
electric current i inside the cell from A to B.

The ramifications of this basic concept are the following:

(1) To complete the circuit of the electric current, an external current i

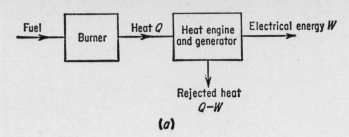

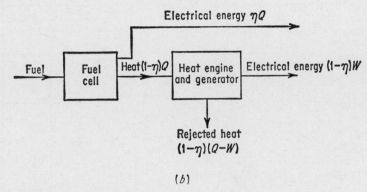

Fig. 7-5. Two Ways of Converting Chemical Energy to Electrical Energy: (a) The Present Method; (b) a Possible Method Using Fuel Cells.

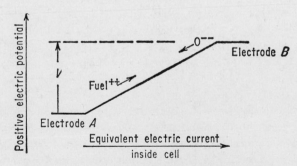

Fig. 7-6. Potential Diagram of a Fuel Cell.

must flow from electrode B to electrode A. A load can be placed in the external circuit to collect the converted electrical energy.

(2) The potential difference V is automatically created by the necessity of maintaining a current i through the load.

(3) The electrical power delivered to the load is Vi, which is exactly the power given up by the ions in climbing the potential hill.

(4) Since a neutral atom of the fuel or oxygen does not give up any of its energy in passing through the potential hill, the neutral atoms must not be allowed to travel from one electrode to the other. Consequently, the electrodes must be separated by some sort of a medium which allows the free passage of one or both types of ions but not the neutral atoms.

(5) In forming the ions, and in the final oxidation of the fuel, three different materials must be brought into simultaneous contact with each other: the oxygen or the fuel; the electrode to supply or to conduct away the electrons; and the medium to supply or to conduct away the ions.

One possible type of medium which meets the requirements of item 4 is an electrolyte which has the fuel or oxygen ions in it but does not dissolve either the fuel or the oxygen. For instance, an acid electrolyte has an abundance of H^+ ions. Although it would be difficult (if possible at all) to find any electrolyte with O^{--} ions, all alkaline electrolytes have $(OH)^-$ ions which would do just as well because of the reaction:

$$O_2 + 2H_2O + 4e \longrightarrow 4(OH)^-$$

The foregoing reaction means that an oxygen molecule combines with two H_2O molecules in the electrolyte and four electrons from the electrode to form four $(OH)^-$ ions in the electrolyte.

As alkaline electrolytes are less corrosive to the electrodes, they have found wider adoption than the acid ones. The only known exception is the ion-exchange membrane cell mentioned in Sec. 7–1. The membrane is more or less an acid electrolyte in quasi-solid state.

The requirement that neither oxygen nor the fuel have any appreciable solubility in the electrolyte is necessary to avoid penetration of neutral atoms through the electrolyte. With this requirement, the reactions are restricted to take place only along lines of triple contact of the electrolyte, the electrode, and the reactant on the same side.

Keeping the preceding five points in mind, we arrive at the basic construction of a fuel cell as shown in Fig. 7–7. There are essentially five layers: The two outside layers are chambers for oxygen or fuel gas. Adjacent to the chamber, are the two electrodes which are made of porous material to allow oxygen and fuel gas to pass through so that lines of triple contact of gas, electrode, and electrolyte can be formed on the inside surfaces of the electrodes. Between the electrodes is the electrolyte.

Although electric current in the external circuit flows from electrode B to electrode A, and electrode B is at a higher positive electric potential than A, *most of the literature on the subject of fuel cells refers to* A *as the anode and* B *as the cathode.* Probably the terminology originated from the electrolysis of water, as the early H_2-O_2 fuel cells were no more than electrolysis in reverse.

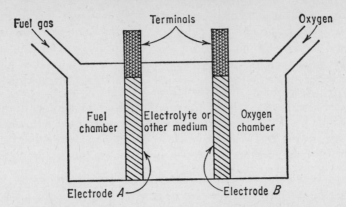

Fig. 7–7. BASIC STRUCTURE OF A FUEL CELL.

7-9. TYPES AND CONSTRUCTIONS OF FUEL CELLS

The construction of a fuel cell is determined primarily by its intended applications:

If a fuel cell is designed for portable power, the essential considerations are weight, efficiency, and cost in this order. Hydrogen and oxygen are used as the fuel and oxidant, respectively, as these elements are most reactive with least complications. Their waste product is H_2O which is the easiest to get rid of.

If a fuel cell is developed for central station power, the essential considerations are fuel cost and efficiency. Carbon and natural gas (CH_4) are the only eligible fuels, and air is used instead of oxygen. Sometimes the fuels are processed first:

$$C + H_2O \longrightarrow CO + H_2$$

$$CH_4 + H_2O \longrightarrow CO + 3H_2$$

As these reactions are reversible, they add little to the entropy. The products are mixtures of CO and H_2, which are more readily used in a fuel cell.

Classified according to their basic structure, there are four distinctively different types:

1. *Direct Type, Low or Medium Temperature, Alkaline Electrolyte*

The basic structure of this type of fuel cell is that of Fig. 7–7. The electrodes are made of porous conductors. Concentrated KOH solution (20% to 40% KOH) is used as the electrolyte. When H_2 is the fuel, the reactions are

At the cathode

$$O_2 + 2H_2O + 4e^- \longrightarrow 4(OH)^-$$

At the anode

$$2H_2 + 4(OH)^- \longrightarrow 4H_2O + 4e^-$$

Overall-all reaction

$$2H_2 + O_2 \longrightarrow 2H_2O$$

The cells would operate for a short period if CO is used as the fuel. The *reaction at the anode* is then

$$2CO + 4(OH)^- \longrightarrow 2H_2O + 2CO_2 + 4e^-$$

The *over-all reaction* is

$$2CO + O_2 \longrightarrow 2CO_2$$

As soon as CO_2 is released, however, it is absorbed by the electrolyte

$$KOH + CO_2 = KHCO_3$$

The electrolyte becomes gradually inoperative as the concentration of $(OH)^-$ ions is greatly reduced by the presence of the bicarbonate. Thus this type of cell is not only unsuitable for operation with CO as fuel, it can also be contaminated by the presence of a trace of CO_2 in H_2 or O_2 as impurity.

The representative developments along this line are

(a) *The Bacon cell.* The cell invented by Francis T. Bacon (1952) of Great Britain is among the earliest of modern fuel cells. It operates at an elevated temperature of about 500°K at a pressure of about 400 to 1,000 psi. The required pressure is above the vapor pressure of the electrolyte to keep it from boiling. Figure 7–8 illustrates the schematic diagram of a Bacon cell developed at the Patterson Moos Division of the Leesona Corporation. The electrodes are made of sintered nickel with finer pores near the electrolyte. A slightly higher gas pressure (than the electrolyte pressure) of 3–5 psi is maintained across the electrode. The gas feeds through the coarse pores but is prevented from bubbling through the fine pores into the electrolyte by the surface tension of the latter. The elevated temperature can be sustained by the heat liberated from the cell reaction itself.

The advantage of the Bacon cell lies in its high current density, about 750 amp per square foot of electrode area at 0.7 volt cell voltage. Its disadvantage lies in the cost for providing a high-pressure system:

(b) *The Union Carbide Cell.* This cell uses activated carbon electrodes which have highly developed surface areas and fine pores throughout. The arrangement of the cell is illustrated in Fig. 7–9. Both electrodes are treated with a repellant to repel the alkaline electrolyte. The electrolyte remains at

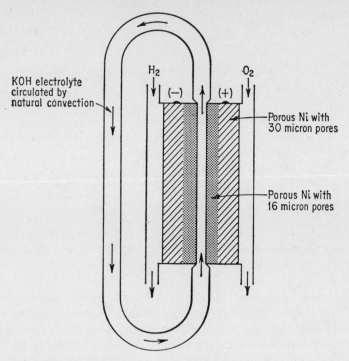

Fig. 7–8. A Bacon-cell (Leesona Moos Laboratories Version).

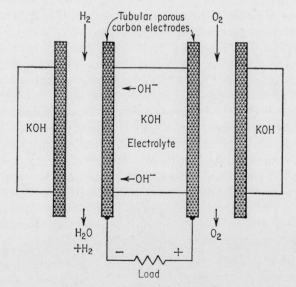

Fig. 7–9. A Union Carbide Cell.

the outer surface while H_2 and O_2 diffuse through the pores of the electrodes. The electrode reactions take place at the outer surfaces of the electrodes.

At low temperature there is a tendency for the cathode reaction to be incomplete

$$O_2 + H_2O + 2e \longrightarrow HO_2^- + OH^-$$

The carbon cathode of the Union Carbide cell is catalytically treated to decompose the peroxide ion

$$2HO_2^- \longrightarrow 2OH^- + O_2$$

As the oxygen yielded is again used up to form hydro-oxide ions, the net reaction is exactly the same as the four ion processes mentioned previously:

$$O_2 + 2H_2O + 4e \longrightarrow 4OH^-$$

The Union Carbide cell has the advantage of operating at normal temperature and pressure (50° to 70°C and atmospheric pressure), and has a fairly high current density of about 100 amp per square foot of electrode area at 0.7 volt. The current density can be drastically improved by using pressurized H_2 and O_2, but this can be done only at too high a cost.

There are many other cells of type (1) in various stages of development: Notable are those developed by Professor Justi of Braunschweig, Germany, by the Allis-Chalmers Company, and by the Electric Storage Company, etc. A common purpose appears to be to obtain high current density at normal operating temperature and pressure. The differences lie essentially in the various catalysts or materials used for the electrodes.

2. *Direct Type, Low-temperature, Ion-exchange Membrane*

The ion-exchange membrane cell developed at the General Electric Company, by W. T. Grubb and L. W. Niedrach has been described in Sec. 7–1, together with its electrode reactions. The distinctive or novel feature of this type of fuel cell is the ion-exchange membrane, which is in effect an acid electrolyte in quasi-solid state.

Hydrogen ions can move from one side of the membrane to the other, but neutral atoms and other types of ions cannot. Each side of the membrane is coated with a layer of noble metals (platinum, palladium) which serves as the electrode as well as an electrocatalyst.

Although the current density of the ion-exchange membrane cells is not as high as some of the other types, about 30 to 50 amp per square foot at 0.7 volt cell voltage, these cells have the advantages of high reliability and a compact construction. There is no possibility for neutral gas to bubble through the membrane, nor is there any danger of a liquid electrolyte drowning the electrode. The membrane including the electrodes is only about $\frac{1}{8}$ in. in thickness, and relatively low current density is made up by the relatively low weight and bulk per unit area of electrode.

Figure 7–10 shows a cell assembly with a plural number of fuel cells connected in series. Although only two cells are shown, the same arrangement can be extended to any number of cells in series. The cells are connected electrically to each other and to the main terminals by a specially formed metal sheet denoted as a bipolar electron collector. It serves as a partition between the H_2 and O_2 gases and also conducts away the heat generated within the cells to the cooling fins below. With this arrangement, up to six cells can be packed in a space of 1 in.

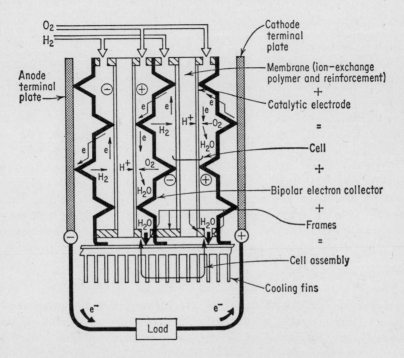

Fig. 7–10. AN ASSEMBLY OF ION EXCHANGE MEMBRANE CELL. (Reprinted from G. A. Phillips, "Status of the Ion-Exchange Membrane Fuel Cell" *Electrical Engineering*, Vol. **81**, No. 3, March 1962, pp. 194–201.)

Air instead of oxygen can be used in an ion-exchange membrane cell specially constructed for this purpose. Instead of having a dead end, air is allowed to flow continuously at the cathode side. The cell then operates at a somewhat reduced current density.

Since the ion-exchange membrane is an acid electrolyte allowing only H^+ ion to pass, the only workable fuel is H_2. This, however, has the further advantage of being immune to CO_2 impurities.

3. *Direct, High-temperature Cells*

As discussed previously, one important requirement of fuel cells for central stations is their ability to use hydrocarbon fuel, which can usually be converted into a mixture of H_2 and CO in a reversible process. The basic requirement then is for the fuel cell to work efficiently with H_2 and CO.

There are two basic difficulties with CO as fuel: First, it is not as reactive as H_2, and the current density is likely to be low. Second, it is quite difficult to find a suitable electrolyte. Since CO does not produce any hydrogen ion, it cannot be used with an acid electrolyte. It cannot be used with an alkaline electrolyte because of the formation of bicarbonates. If a carbonate is used as the electrolyte, as it is a weak alkali, the cell reactivity is likely to be lower still.

One way to resolve the difficulties cited is to use fused carbonates as the electrolyte and to operate the cell at high temperature to increase its reactivity. Aqueous electrolytes are not practical at temperatures much above $500°K$ owing to the rapid increase in vapor pressure. Similar limitation on fused carbonates, however, occurs at a much higher temperature. In order to obtain as active an electrolyte as possible, Li, Na, and K carbonates or a mixture of these are generally used.

The electrode reactions are as follows:

Cathode reaction

$$O_2 + 2CO_2 + 4e^- \longrightarrow 2CO_3^{--}$$

Anode reaction

$$H_2 + CO_3^{--} \longrightarrow H_2O + CO_2 + 2e^-$$

$$CO + CO_3^{--} \longrightarrow 2CO_2 + 2e^-$$

As H_2 is more active than CO, it is far more rapidly depleted than the latter. As the remaining gas can be recirculated and used over and over again, however, the carbon monoxide gas is eventually used up.

The electrode materials must not be corroded under the high temperature operating condition nor must they develop resistive films. The materials used in various experimental cells include a wide selection of metals and oxides: NiO, Cu_2O, Pt, Fe, Ni, Co, Cu, Cr, Mn, and Ag.

The current densities of various experimental cells range from 20–100 amp per square foot at 0.7 volt cell voltage. The operational lives are relatively short, however, owing to corrosion of construction materials and loss of electrolyte through vaporization.

4. *The Indirect or Redox Cells*

Redox cells are so named because fuel and oxidant are used to regenerate two electrolytic fluids instead of reacting at the electrodes directly. The basic construction of a redox cell is illustrated in Fig. 7–11. The cell is

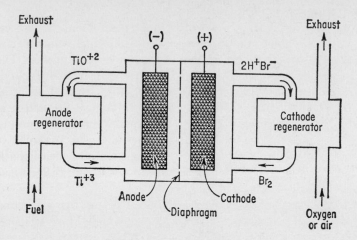

Fig. 7–11. A REDOX CELL.

divided by a diaphragm which allows free passage of H⁺ ion. A pair of electrolytes are circulated separately at two sides of the cell through two regenerators where they react with the fuel and oxygen.

In a redox cell developed at the General Electric Company, H_2 and O_2 are used as the fuel and oxidant. The reactions are

Anode reaction

$$2Ti^{+++} + 2H_2O \longrightarrow 2TiO^{++} + 4H^+ + 2e^-$$

Anode regeneration

$$2TiO^{++} + 2H^+ + H_2 \longrightarrow 2Ti^{+++} + 2H_2O$$

Cathode reaction

$$Br_2 + 2e^- \longrightarrow 2Br^-$$

Cathode regeneration

$$2H^+ + 2Br^- + \tfrac{1}{2}O_2 \longrightarrow Br_2 + H_2O$$

The over-all reactions of the cell are

Anode side

$$H_2 \longrightarrow 2H^+ + 2e^-$$

Cathode side

$$\tfrac{1}{2}O_2 + 2e^- + 2H^+ \longrightarrow H_2O$$

The operating current density is moderately high. The operating life is relatively short, however, and the cell is not in as advanced a stage of development as the ion-exchange membrane cell.

In a cell developed at the King's College, London, coal powder and air are used as the fuel and oxidant, respectively.

The reactions are

Anode reaction

$$2Sn^{++} \longrightarrow 2Sn^{++++} + 4e^-$$

Anode regeneration

$$2Sn^{++++} + 2H_2O + C \longrightarrow CO_2 + 2Sn^{++} + 4H^{++}$$

Cathode reaction

$$2Br_2 + 4e^- \longrightarrow 4Br^-$$

Cathode regeneration

$$4Br^- + 4H^+ + O_2 \longrightarrow 2Br_2 + 2H_2O$$

The over-all reactions of the cell are
Anode side

$$C + 2H_2O \longrightarrow CO_2 + 4H^+ + 4e^-$$

Cathode side

$$4H^+ + O_2 + 4e^- \longrightarrow 2H_2O$$

The King's College cell has relatively low open-circuit voltage and low current density, about 10 amp per square foot at 0.62 volt cell voltage.

7-10. OPERATING CHARACTERISTICS OF FUEL CELLS

The terminal voltage of a fuel cell depends on its current density and operating temperature. A typical voltage versus current density curve is given in Fig. 7–12. The voltage E_r is the reversible emf of the process given by

$$E_r = \frac{1}{ne} \sum_i n_i F_i = \frac{-\Delta F}{ne} \tag{7-15}$$

Owing to various hindrances at the electrodes, however, the reversible emf is generally greater than the actual no-load voltage E_n:

At very light loads, the cell voltage drops sharply. Then there is a linear range from A to B which usually covers the operating range of the fuel cell. Beyond B, the cell voltage again drops sharply with increasing current density. This curve is usually referred to in the literature as the *polarization curve*.

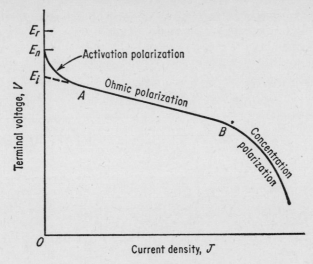

Fig. 7–12. Cell Voltage versus Current Density.

The reason for the initial drop, or *activation polarization*, is not exactly known. It is probably due to various irreversible effects at the electrodes and can be regarded as the "motive force" required to make the ions leave one electrode and approach another. The dominant factor for the linear drop in the operating range AB is the ohmic resistance in the electrolyte. It is referred to in the literature as *ohmic polarization*. Beyond point B, electrostatic effects due to concentration gradient in the electrolyte begin to limit the current. The latter gives rise to unbalanced local charge which acts in much the same way as the space-charge effect in a vacuum tube. Another possible contributing factor is the density gradient of the reactants in the pores especially when there are impurities present. The lumped term for these two effects is *concentration polarization*.

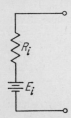

Fig. 7–13. Equivalent Circuit of a Fuel Cell.

The internal emf E_i is not the no-load voltage E_n but is obtained by extrapolating the linear range AB. When operating in the linear range, the fuel cell can be represented as an internal emf E_i in series with an internal resistance R_i, as illustrated in Fig. 7–13. The resistance R_i is equal to the slope of AB in Fig. 7–12 divided by the electrode area of the cell.

According to published data, typical values of R_i for a fuel cell with 1 sq ft of electrode area is 0.004 to 0.008 ohm for the ion-exchange membrane cell operating at slightly above room temperature and 1 atm pressure, and 0.00035 ohm for a Bacon cell operating at 800 psi and 240°C. The internal emf for both cells is about 0.93 volt.

Fig. 7–14 gives the reversible emf versus temperature curves for H_2-O_2 cell and CO-O_2 cell. These curves are readily calculated from the free energy data for the different materials. The reversible emf, however, is only part of the story. As the reactivity of a cell is generally increased by a rise in the operating temperature, the terminal voltage at a reasonable load is likely to increase with temperature rather than decrease.

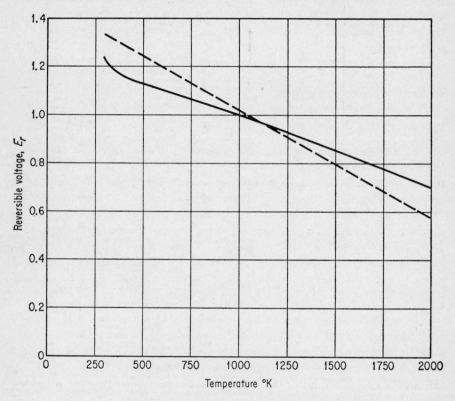

Fig. 7–14. REVERSIBLE VOLTAGE VERSUS TEMPERATURE: SOLID CURVE, $H_2 + \frac{1}{2}O_2 \rightarrow H_2O$; BROKEN CURVE, $CO + \frac{1}{2}O_2 \rightarrow CO_2$.

In most fuel cells, the loss through leakage of neutral molecules across the electrolyte is kept at a negligible value. Consequently, the efficiency of the cell is proportional to the cell voltage, V:

$$\text{eff} = \frac{neV}{(-\Delta H)} = \frac{V}{E_h} \tag{7-58}$$

7-11. BASIC REQUIREMENTS AND A SUMMARY OF THE MEASURES TO MEET THESE REQUIREMENTS

The preceding sections have discussed the advantages of a fuel cell: It is basically a simple device and compares favorably in terms of efficiency, weight, etc., with existing power plants as well as with batteries of the primary and secondary types. What then keeps it from wide adoption commercially? Some basic requirements must be met for successful operation of a fuel cell, and as yet there is no way of meeting these requirements economically.

The basic requirements can be grouped into two categories:

1. *Reactivity Requirements*

These are the requirements on the positive side about the desired reaction itself. The two important ones under this category are

(a) *Completeness of the reaction*

The fuel not only should be used up in the proper way, but should be in the stage of lowest free energy per atom before it is discharged. For instance, if in a fuel cell using carbon or hydrocarbon compounds, some carbon monoxide is discharged as the waste product instead of carbon dioxide, less than half of the free energy per carbon atom is utilized.

A more serious defect is the leakage of neutral molecules through the medium or electrolyte. The "short-circuited" reaction represents not only a loss in utilizable energy, it could touch off an explosion in most fuel cells, e.g., the H_2-O_2 type.

(b) *Speed of the reaction*

The speed, or rate at which ionization and final oxidation can take place, and the rate at which ions can be transported across the medium impose a limit on the current density (current per unit area of electrodes) of the fuel cell and also determine the terminal voltage, or actual output voltage of the cell, for any given current density. This point has been discussed in Sec. 7–10.

The most serious bottleneck on the speed of reaction is the electrode reactivity. As discussed in Sec. 7–8, the reactions can take place only along the *lines* of triple contact of the electrode with the electrolyte and one of the reactants. Mathematicians know only too well that any countable number of lines cannot add to a surface of finite area; the "site" of the reaction is just too small compared to that of normal chemical reactions which usually take place either on an entire surface or in an entire volume. Fortunately, the "lines" of contact are not exactly one-dimensional since, as long as electrode, electrolyte, and fuel gas (or oxygen) are brought within atomic distances of each other, reactions can and do take place. Contrary to the dire predictions from overly simplified mathematics, our "lines" of contact do add up to an appreciable surface, though it takes much fabrication to do this.

In most fuel cells two corrective measures are employed: (a) enlarging the site of reaction by using porous electrodes with numerous fine pores on the surface in contact with the electrolyte; (b) increasing the effectiveness of the sites of reaction by using activated electrodes, catalysts, and/or high temperature and pressure.

The problem of transportation of the ions across the electrolyte is solved by using highly concentrated and active electrolytes. For instance, concentrated KOH electrolytes are used for $(OH)^-$ ions. The difficulty does not lie in solving the problem itself but in solving it in conjunction with the invariance requirements.

2. Invariance Requirements

To insure long life, the fuel cell should not change with usage. To be specific, the invariance requirements can be itemized as

(a) No corrosion or side reactions
(b) Invariant electrolyte and electrodes
(c) Adequate disposal of waste products and impurities in fuel and oxygen
(d) Proper balance of gas and electrolyte inside the electrodes

The preceding items are not meant to be independent. Of course, if the electrolyte corrodes the electrodes, the fuel cell will not last long. There are also more subtle effects, for instance, the waste products of cells using hydrocarbon fuels are H_2O and CO_2. If not adequately disposed of, H_2O could dilute the electrolyte, and CO_2 could dissolve in an alkali-based electrolyte to form bicarbonates. Impurities in the fuel and oxygen could poison the catalysts. In a fuel cell using air, the leftover nitrogen could block fresh air from entering the pores of the electrodes and thus cut off the supply of oxygen. Even without foreign matter, the pores can be gradually filled with the electrolyte or with gas; consequently there is a loss of the lines of triple contacts, and with it, the loss of electrode reactivity. Note that the gradation of pore size in the Bacon cell and the use of repellant in the Union Carbide cell are means to insure the lines of triple contact.

Generally, the invariance requirements are in conflict with the reactivity requirements. The latter can be met through strong alkali electrolytes, high temperature, and pressure—all of which tend to cause or accentuate corrosion. The invariance requirements also constitute a substantial hurdle in the way of using low-cost fuel and air because of the various side effects and the difficulties of disposing of a variety of waste materials originated from the impurities.

REFERENCES

1. Lewis, G. N., M. Randall, K. S. Pitzer, and Leo Brewer, *Thermodynamics*, 2nd ed., pp. 138–371. New York: McGraw-Hill Book Co., 1961.

2. Rossini, F. D., *Chemical Thermodynamics*, pp. 119–51; 347–64. New York: John Wiley & Sons, 1950.

3. Kaye, J., and J. A. Welsh, *Direct Conversion of Heat to Electricity*, Chap. 23. New York: John Wiley & Sons, 1960.

4. Phillips, G. A., "Status of Development and Future Prospects for the Ion-Exchange Membrane Fuel Cell," *Elec. Eng.*, **81**, No. 3 (March, 1962), 194–201.

5. Liebhafsky, H. A., and L. W. Niedrach. "Fuel Cells," *Jour. Franklin Institute*, **269**, No. 4 (April, 1960), 257–67.

6. —— and W. T. Grubb, Jr., "The Fuel Cell in Space," *Amer. Rocket Soc. Jour.* September, 1961, pp. 1183–90.

7. Goldstein, M., "Hydrox Fuel Cells and Their Application in Aircraft and Space Vehicles," paper presented at the Aircraft Electrical Society meeting, February, 1959.

PROBLEMS

7-1. At 1000°K and 1 atm pressure, the total and free energies released by the two reactions

(1) $C + \frac{1}{2}O_2 \longrightarrow CO$

(2) $C + O_2 \longrightarrow CO_2$

are
$$(\Delta H)_1 = -26.8 \text{ kcal/mole}$$
$$(\Delta H)_2 = -94.4 \text{ kcal/mole}$$
$$(\Delta F)_1 = -47.8 \text{ kcal/mole}$$
$$(\Delta F)_2 = -94.6 \text{ kcal/mole}$$

Calculate the reversible emf E_r, and $(\partial E_r/\partial T)_p$ for the following reaction:

$$CO + \tfrac{1}{2}O_2 \longrightarrow CO_2 + 2eE_r + Q$$

Is heat released or absorbed by the process?
What is the maximum efficiency E_r/E_h?

7-2. Repeat the calculations in Prob. 7-1 for the following cases:

(a)
$$p_{CO} = 10 \text{ atm}$$
$$p_{O_2} = 2 \text{ atm}$$
$$p_{CO_2} = 0.1 \text{ atm}$$

(b)
$$p_{CO} = 1 \text{ atm}$$
$$p_{O_2} = 0.2 \text{ atm}$$
$$p_{CO_2} = 0.5 \text{ atm}$$

7-3. One type of galvanic cell is obtained by immersing a platinum electrode and a silver electrode in HCl solution. The reactions taking place at the electrodes are

Silver electrode
$$Ag + Cl^- \longrightarrow AgCl + e$$

Platinum electrode
$$H^+ + e \longrightarrow \tfrac{1}{2}H_2$$

Bates and Bower measured the emf of these cells with great care in the temperature range 0–90°C, and obtained the following result:

$$E = 0.35510 - 0.3422 \times 10^{-4}t - 3.2347 \times 10^{-6}t^2 + 6.314 \times 10^{-9}t^3 \text{ volt}$$

where t is the temperature in degrees centigrade. Assume E to be the reversible emf and calculate ΔF and ΔH for the reaction

$$Ag + HCl \longrightarrow AgCl + \tfrac{1}{2}H_2$$

7-4. The molality of a given aqueous solution is defined as the number of moles of the solute in 1 kg of water. In dilute aqueous solutions, the thermodynamic functions H and S of the solute vary with the molality in exactly the same way as H and S of an ideal gas do with its pressure. Bates and Bower made their measurements with 0.1 molar solution of HCl. What is the anticipated expression for E if the concentration of HCl is 0.01 mole? 0.5 mole?

7-5. In a reversible chemical reaction,

$$aA + bB \rightleftharpoons cC + dD$$

where A, B, C, and D are different solutes in the same aqueous solution, and a, b, c, and d are small integers. Show that

$$\frac{M_A^a M_B^b}{M_C^c M_D^d} = K(T)$$

where $K(T)$ is the equilibrium constant and is a function of temperature only; the M's are the molar concentrations of the solutes.

Find a similar solution when the reactants are different kinds of ideal gas.

7-6. The third law of thermodynamics states that U and S are zero at 0°K. Suppose there is an ideal gas which obeys the ideal gas law down to 0°K. Show that U is finite but S is infinite at any given non-zero temperature.

7–7. Lewis and Randall gave the following empirical expression for the heat capacity of a gas at 1 atm pressure in the temperature range 298°K to 2000°K [1, p. 66]:

$$C_p = a + bT + cT^{-2} \qquad (\text{P } 7\text{–}7\text{–}1)$$

Given H_{298} and S_{298} as the enthalpy and entropy of the gas respectively at 298°K. Find expressions of H, S, and F at 1 atm pressure as functions of T.

7–8. In an electrochemical process, the Cp of the gases is given by Eq. (P 7–7–1), but the relation $pV = mRT$ still holds for the different gases. How should Eq. (7–27) be modified?

7–9. The process of changing graphite into diamond

$$\text{C (graphite)} \longrightarrow \text{C (diamond)}$$

requires an *increase* in free energy

$$\Delta F = 685 \text{ cal/mole}$$

at 298°K and 1 atm pressure. The density of diamond is 3.52 gm/cm³, and the density of graphite is 2.25 gm/cm³. Assume that neither the densities nor the internal energies, U_i, change with pressure and estimate the required pressure to give $\Delta F = 0$.

7–10. Show that in the linear range of operation of a fuel cell

$$P = \frac{E_h \eta (E_i - E_h \eta) A}{R}$$

where η is the efficiency of the fuel cell as defined by Eq. (7–58), R is the equivalent resistance of a fuel cell with 1 sq ft of electrode area, and A is the total area of the fuel cell.

7–11. Find expressions of

(a) maximum power P_m
(b) η at maximum power
(c) current density J at maximum power

in terms of E_i, E_h, and R

7–12. In space applications, an important concern is to minimize the total weight for a given mission. The simplest case to consider is supplying a constant power P for a period T. The required weight is the sum of three parts:

$$\text{Weight of fuel and tank} = \frac{PT}{\eta(-\Delta H)} \cdot \frac{n_f W_f}{\xi_f}$$

$$\text{Weight of oxygen and tank} = \frac{PT}{\eta(-\Delta H)} \cdot \frac{n_0 W_0}{\xi_0}$$

$$\text{Weight of fuel cell} = W_c A + W_b$$

where n_f and n_0 are the number of moles of fuel and oxygen per mole of reaction, where $(-\Delta H)$ is the energy released per mole of reaction in joules; W_f and W_0 are the molecular weights of the fuel molecule and oxygen, ξ_f and ξ_0 are the packing factors (net weight/gross weight including tank) for the fuel and oxygen, W_c is the weight per unit of electrode area, W_b is a fixed weight (e.g., weight of controls), and A is the total electrode area of all the fuel cells whether connected in series or in parallel.

Show that for minimum total weight, each fuel cell should be operated at a point of efficiency

$$\eta = \frac{E_i}{E_h} \cdot \frac{\sqrt{C_1/C_2}}{1 + \sqrt{C_1/C_2}}$$

where

$$C_1 = \frac{RW_c}{E_h E_i} + \frac{T}{(-\Delta H)} \cdot \left(\frac{n_f W_f}{\xi_f} + \frac{n_0 W_0}{\xi_0} \right)$$

$$C_2 = \frac{RW_c}{E_h E_i}$$

APPENDIX A

Conversion Factors

	MKS units	CGS units	English units	
Length	1 m	100 cm	39.37 in.	3.2808 ft
Mass	1 kg	1,000 grams	2.2046 lb	0.0684 slug
Energy	1 joule	10^7 ergs, 0.239 cal	0.73756 ft-lb	0.94783×10^{-3} Btu
Power	1 watt	10^7 ergs/sec	1/746 h.p.	
Force	1 newton	10^5 dynes	0.2247 lb	3.6 oz
Electric Charge	1 coulomb	0.1 emu, 3×10^9 esu	1 coulomb	
Electric Potential	1 volt	10^8 emu $\frac{1}{300}$ esu	1 volt	
Magnetic Flux	1 weber	10^8 lines	10^8 lines	
Magnetization	1 weber/m²	10,000 gauss	64,500 lines/in.²	
Magnetic Field Intensity	1 amp-turn/m	$4\pi \times 10^{-3}$ oersted	39.37 amp-turn/in.	

APPENDIX B

Useful Physical Constants

Name of Constant	Symbol	Value
Electron charge	e	1.6021×10^{-19} coulomb
Electron rest mass	m	9.1086×10^{-31} kg
Velocity of light	c	2.998×10^{8} m/sec
Planck's constant	h	6.625×10^{-34} joule-sec
Boltzmann constant	k	1.3804×10^{-23} joule/deg
Avogadro's number	N_0	6.0247×10^{26} molecules per kilogram mole
Faraday constant		96520 coulomb per mole; 9.652×10^{6} coulombs per kilogram mole
Gas constant	R	8314 joules/deg kg mole 1987 cal/deg kg mole
1 calorie		4.185 joules
1 electron-volt	ev	1.6021×10^{-19} joule
1 atomic mass unit		931.14 mev (million ev)
Energy/degree	k/e	8.616×10^{-5} ev/degree
Electrical susceptibility of vacuum	ϵ_0	$(1/36\pi) \times 10^{-9}$ farad/m
Magnetic permeability of vacuum	μ_0	$4\pi \times 10^{-7}$ henry/m

INDEX